D1206419

MEMORIES OF TEILHARD DE CHARDIN

HELMUT DE TERRA

Memories of Teilhard de Chardin

TRANSLATED FROM
THE GERMAN BY
J. MAXWELL BROWNJOHN

HARPER & ROW, PUBLISHERS

New York and Evanston

MEMORIES OF TEILHARD DE CHARDIN. Originally published in German under the title MEIN WEG MIT TEILHARD DE CHARDIN by C. H. Beck'sche Verlagsbuchhandlung, Munich, 1962. For information address Harper & Row, Publishers, Incorporated, 49 East 33rd Street, New York 16, N. Y.

FIRST EDITION

LIBRARY OF CONGRESS CATALOG CARD NUMBER: 65-10369

Contents

Foreword

MY MEETING WITH PIERRE TEILHARD DE CHARDIN was one of those experiences which steadily gain in importance. So many people have been enriched by Teilhard's writings in the time that has elapsed since his death that I cannot resist the temptation to record my memories of him, his participation in my Asian expeditions and our occasional encounters in America. I feel impelled to share my thoughts and impressions with those whose study of his works has inspired them with a wish to know how he operated as a scientist. Anyone familiar with his work will appreciate the especial desirability of this, since his wealth of ideas, though sustained by profound religious faith, was founded upon the scientific studies which occupied his entire life and claimed his energies until he was past the age of seventy.

Teilhard acquired his views on the origin and evolution of life, in particular human life, by wielding his magnifying glass and geologist's hammer in almost every corner of the world. The world was his laboratory. In my view, no one can form any true conception of his grand and fervent quest for knowledge of man's destiny without also becoming acquainted with him as he was in his professional milieu. To know how he behaved under canvas in the Himalayas and Burma, in desert and jungle, seems to me to be quite as germane to a closer acquaintanceship with his rich personality as any purely biographical particulars.[1] It may be that one has to be a scientist oneself, or at least familiar with the methods employed by the geological sciences, to appreciate the full extent of Teilhard's devotion to field-work. The vast horizons which the latter opened up for him encouraged him to make far-reaching pronouncements on the destiny of mankind:

> The Earth, (he wrote)[2] is still far from having completed its sidereal evolution. True, we can imagine all sorts of catastrophes which might intervene to cut short this great development. But for 300 million years now, Life has been going on paradoxically in the midst of improbability. Does that not indicate that it is marching forward, sustained by some complicity in the motive forces of the Universe? . . .
>
> Progress, if it is to continue, will not happen by itself. Evolution, by the very mechanism of its syntheses, is constantly acquiring greater freedom.
>
> In practice, what steps must we take in relation to this forward march? I see two, which can be summarized in five words: *a great hope, in common.*
>
> a) First, *a great hope.* This must be born spontaneously in every generous soul in face of the antici-

[1] See the biographies by Claude Cuénot: *Pierre Teilhard de Chardin*, Paris 1958; and Nicolas Corte: *La vie et l'âme de Teilhard de Chardin*, Paris 1957 (English translation 1960).

[2] *Cahiers Teilhard de Chardin I*, 'Building the Earth', Éditions du Seuil, Paris 1958, p. 29 et seq.

pated work, and it also represents the essential *impetus* without which nothing will be done. A passionate love of growth, of being, that is what we need. Down with the cowards and the sceptics, the pessimists and the unhappy, the weary and the stagnant.

b) *In common.* On this point also the history of Life is decisive. There is only one way which leads upwards; the one which, through greater organization, leads to greater synthesis and unity. Here again, then, down with the pure individualists, the egoists, who expect to grow by excluding or diminishing their brothers, individually, nationally or racially. Our hope will only be operative if it is expressed in greater cohesion and greater human solidarity.

The future of the Earth is in our hands. How shall we decide?

Surrounded by contemporary revolutions in scientific thought and aware of their momentous consequences, Teilhard felt called upon to create a great synthesis of man in the cosmos. The fact that he required means other than those which science could provide denoted a measure of mental affinity with other eminent scientists. It was only while drafting the last chapter of this book, in which I mention a few of the scientists who happened to figure in my conversations with Teilhard, that I became fully alive to his great importance. He wanted to awaken a new vitality and stronger awareness of man's common destiny which could invest life with meaning and purpose. To me, this summons seems to stem less from the instinct of self-preservation or from fear born of weakness than from the sense of endeavour which has characterized the man of faith from time immemorial.

Teilhard shared with other scientists an ability to 'feel' his way into terrain whose history he had to know in order to derive special meaning from the geological records of life there. Anyone who, like him, acquires a knowledge of the earth that is 'tangible' in the truest sense of the word, anyone who tries to grasp its meaning by dint of extreme physical exertion, has to traverse a succession of ideas before arriving at an over-all view. Once, when questioned about Teilhard's research, I felt that the only way of conveying my impression of it was to say that he always stooped over the ground so as to see the sky above. By this I meant that he had a special ability to understand man's present condition and infer future developments from the sum total of the past.

In recording my experiences with Teilhard I have drawn upon my own notes and a few unpublished letters which were kindly placed at my disposal by the Fondation P. Teilhard de Chardin of Paris, through the kindness of M. Claude Cuénot. In order to place my meetings with Teilhard in perspective I have considered it necessary to include certain extracts from his *Letters from a Traveller* and from publications relating to particular impressions and scientific studies. The knowledge that he gleaned important information about human prehistory by taking part in my Asian expeditions affords me even keener satisfaction because this helped him to formulate his ideas on the origin of man.

A Brief Summary of a Full Life

MARIE-JOSEPH-PIERRE TEILHARD DE CHARDIN WAS born in his family's château in the small village of Sarcenat (Auvergne) on 1 May 1881. He was the fourth of eleven children and the scion of a family which could trace its ancestry back to a certain Astorg Teilhard, who was elevated to the petty nobility in the year 1538. The area is one of the loveliest in France, dotted with massive and ancient mountains of volcanic rock, fertile valleys and places of historic interest. A few kilometres distant lies the ancient city of Clermont-Ferrand, where Pope Urban II launched the First Crusade and sent it to the very gates of Jerusalem with the ringing affirmation '*Dieu li volt*'—'God wills it'.

Teilhard's father, Emmanuel, a man in whom sense of duty, religious faith and a thirst for knowledge were harmoniously combined, became his example. He encouraged the boy to collect natural history specimens. When his mother, Berthe-Adèle, a great-grand-niece of Voltaire, died in 1936, Teilhard lovingly confessed that he had inherited 'the depths of his being' from her. At the age of sixty-nine, he recalled a peculiar feature of his childhood. 'To be really happy I needed a knowledge of *Some One Essential Thing*, compared with which all else seemed supplementary or even ornamental.' In his childish way, he made a piece of iron the outward manifestation of this Something, a twofold symbol of God and matter which he revered 'with a keen sense of devotion in which a number of associations were mingled; and my whole spiritual life has been nothing more than the development of these.'[1] In the purity of childish intuition, he had become aware of the dualism of matter.

In accordance with family tradition, Teilhard entered the Jesuit school at Mongré (Dept. Rhône) at the age of eleven. The teachers there reported on the dreamy and deeply religious nature of the boy, who had, even at this early stage, decided to enter the priesthood. As a gifted student of eighteen, he became a novice at the Jesuit college in Aix-en-Provence, where he received a thorough grounding in theology and the classics before developing an interest in science and, in particular, geology. When the anti-clerical sentiments prevailing in 1901 temporarily drove the Jesuit Order out of France, Teilhard moved to a seminary on the island of Jersey, where he remained for four years. This marked the start of his training in chemistry, physics and geology, and in 1904 his name was mentioned for the first time as joint author of a paper on geological and mineralogical studies in Jersey.

We next meet Teilhard on the staff of a Jesuit college in Cairo, where he taught for three years. This was the origin of his fruitful contact with the East, which lured him back repeatedly until he was fifty-five. Familiarity with ancient Egypt, which aroused archaeological interest in others, encouraged the young teacher to

[1] Corte, pp. 3-4.

collect stones, fossils and shells in the Nile Valley. An excursion to the oasis of Fayum in 1907 turned his attention to fossil vertebrates, on which he published a paper two years later. However, he had to complete his theological training at a Jesuit college near Hastings before being ordained in 1911. His first publications on fossil vertebrates and plants signalled his emergence from the amateur phase into the world of the professional. A visit to the site of the Piltdown Man—a hoax that remained undetected until the 'fifties—inspired him to write an article of some substance. At the same time, he was enthralled by the theological problems raised by his study of the Bible and other sources, believing that ancient texts by prominent theologians of the past could give rise to new interpretations of cosmogeny.[2]

Teilhard spent the two years preceding the outbreak of the First World War as a pupil of the distinguished palaeontologist Marcellin Boule in Paris. It was at the Institut de Paléontologie Humaine, directed by Boule, that he embarked on the academic studies which were to bring him into contact with such eminent prehistorians as Abbé Henri Breuil and Hugo Obermaier, whom he accompanied on a visit to the famous Altamira Caves in Spain. He also attended lectures on geology and mineralogy. Although initially exempt from mobilization in August 1914, he felt an urge to see active service. After a year's stay in England he went into action in June 1915 as a stretcher-bearer attached to a Moroccan regiment on the Western Front. He served in this capacity in almost all the major battles, during which his courage won the gratitude of innumerable soldiers and his

[2] Cuénot, p. 27.

country's formal recognition. After a brief spell in England at the end of the war, the young priest, now an officer of the Légion d'Honneur and holder of the Croix de Guerre and Médaille Militaire, returned to the tranquillity of the Paris Museum, where he worked on the thesis that gained him his doctorate in 1922. In this, he described the evolutionary principle in certain mammalian groups during the Tertiary period and openly advocated research into the origin of man ('faith requires the whole truth'), on which his teacher, Boule, was currently compiling a book. It may have been at this stage, or even earlier, that Teilhard became acquainted with Henri Bergson's concept of 'creative evolution'.

In 1923, after a brief period of training in Paris, he was invited to collaborate on geological and prehistoric research in China by Père Émile Licent, a fellow-Jesuit. Licent had established a museum at Tientsin which also served him as a research centre. At this period, American scientists based on Peking were conducting large-scale expeditions into Central Asia, where the indefatigable explorer Sven Hedin was reputed to be again at work. China had become a centre of scientific exploration, and offered great opportunities to a man with Teilhard's first-class training. By the summer of 1923 he was already accompanying Licent into the Ordos area and the Gobi Desert, where he discovered hitherto unknown palaeolithic cultures. These shed an entirely new light on the prehistory of East Asia and led, six years later, thanks to Teilhard's untiring co-operation, to the discovery of the fossil Peking Man. Since the scientific spoils of his first expeditions in China belonged to the Paris Museum, he resumed his teaching activities in Paris before returning to Peking in 1926.

In the following year Teilhard was entrusted, under American sponsorship and in collaboration with Chinese, European and American fellow-specialists, with extending the study of fossil man in China. The Institute for Cenozoic Research, sponsored by the Rockefeller Foundation, granted him every facility for carrying out this great task, in which he enjoyed the collaboration of distinguished scholars, notably the brilliant Canadian anatomist Dr Davidson Black, Professors Breuil, Barbour, Grabau and Granger, and the Chinese palaeontologist C. C. Young. As a result of explorations in the immense basin of the Yellow River and of laboratory work in Peking and Tientsin, the mists began to recede from a geological picture which gave a clearer view than ever before of the zoological status of early man. The skulls and tools which were dug up with such care near Peking soon encouraged Teilhard to declare that 'the discovery of Sinanthropus represents an important victory for those who uphold the extension of Transformism to the human zoological form.' [3] At the same time, he warned against drawing inferences about the actual nature of mature man from 'embryogenesis', that is to say, the early phases of human development. According to him, the postulate of man's transcendent importance in the over-all picture of evolution was in no way shaken by the anatomical characteristics discernible in the evolutionary stages of early man.

Despite Teilhard's enthusiastic and distinguished participation in such research, he felt that he must not

[3] Corte, p. 40.

neglect his theological and philosophical work. In demonstrating that the latest discoveries in physics required scientists to apply their accounts of the empirical world to its spiritual content, he began to evolve the idea of a kind of spiritual cosmogeny. From the geological aspect, the general evolution of life acquires meaning only if man is regarded as its supreme and unique manifestation.

In 1930 Teilhard took part in the American Museum of Natural History's last expedition to the Gobi Desert. This resulted in visits to the United States and France, where he undertook to join the Citroën-Haardt Expedition to West Central Asia. Upon completing his journeys of exploration in China during 1932, he entered on a new phase in his career. By now an expert of international standing in the field of Asian prehistory, geology and vertebrate palaeontology, he became an adviser to various fellow-scientists. At the same time, he developed his philosophical ideas. Attendance at the International Geological Congress in summer 1933 augmented his contacts with American scholars and scientific institutes. Shortly thereafter he temporarily took charge of the Institute at Peking, which had been orphaned by the sudden death of Dr Black and was ultimately entrusted to the care of the distinguished German anatomist Dr Franz Weidenreich. Teilhard's wish to extend the insights into man's origin which he had gained in China prompted him to join expeditions to India, Burma and Java (1935, 1937-38) conducted by myself and sponsored by American institutes. Between these trips he visited the new fossil sites in Java and attended a congress at Philadelphia. The years between

1939 and 1946 were largely devoted to literary and laboratory work in Peking. *Le Phénomène humain* and *Le Groupe zoölogique humain* were written during this period.

After his return to Paris in 1946, Teilhard began increasingly to expound his views on science, evolution and the origin of man at conferences and in personal discussions with distinguished figures. UNESCO circles in Paris furnished him with some stimulating personal contacts, among them the British zoologist Dr Julian Huxley. The measure of his reputation in Paris is indicated by his election to membership of the Academy of Sciences and his brief tenure of office with the Geological Society. Nevertheless, his relations with the Church remained so strained that he eventually decided to move to America. 1951 saw him in South Africa, where he spent a short time inspecting prehominid and palaeolithic sites, and he later visited Africa again for the same purpose. His latter years, which he spent in New York, afforded him many opportunities to expound his ideas on the origin and destiny of man to various conferences, always in the succinct style so characteristic of him.

He died in New York during the afternoon of Easter Sunday, 10 April 1955.

Memories of Teilhard de Chardin

MY FIRST MEETING WITH TEILHARD AT THE INTERnational Geological Congress in Washington in 1933 was attributable to our common interests. These had, until then, developed quite independently of each other, although we had both undertaken geological expeditions to Central Asia in the course of which we had come upon traces of early man. Those who are familiar with Teilhard's writings will appreciate that we were bound to meet sooner or later. I might add that I had been acquainted with his scientific work for years and knew, in particular, of the part he had played in discovering the fossil Peking Man. Nevertheless, I should not have gathered from his specialized publications that their author was not only a prehistorian but also, in large measure, a philosopher and seer. I cannot pretend, either, that he gave me any opportunity, during the Congress, to get to know this highly attractive side of his nature. We were far too engrossed in discussions which ranged, so far as our existing knowledge permitted, over the geological panorama of human evolution in Asia. He had heard the lecture on geological affinities between the Alps and

Himalayas with which I had introduced myself to the delegates as an Asiologist.

To me, who had already paid two visits to Asia, Teilhard and the party of delegates from China seemed to be wrapped in a very special nimbus. In such company, one seemed to have been miraculously transported to the Gobi Desert or Peking. The burning topic of the day was the discovery of Peking Man's remains, which were held to be the earliest fossil traces of our ancestors in Asia, and I remember someone saying that a Dr Davidson Black of Peking wore the fossil tooth of that primitive human being on a chain beneath his waistcoat. This may not sound as exciting now, in the age of atomic and cosmic research, as it did to us then—yet who can help feeling a certain curiosity about the origin of man at this particular juncture, when human intellect is tackling the exploration and conquest of space? Where did human self-awareness come from, when did it first declare itself and what was the first manifestation of its existence?

What especially interested Teilhard about my report on this occasion was the fact that I had discovered a number of Stone-Age artefacts in Kashmir and the foothills of the Himalayas during 1932. Insignificant though these finds were, they denoted the presence of primitive man in an area noted by experts for its abundance of fossils, among them relics of anthropoid apes. The discovery of the first traces of early men in North-West India was a geological configuration which suddenly opened up great prospects of clarifying human prehistory in Asia. One has to be alive to the importance of Teilhard's interpretation of man to understand why he was so interested in this part of India. He shared this interest with another scientist, the one who was reputed to wear a human fossil under his waistcoat, a short, slim man of Canadian origin who had been assigned to Peking as an anatomist by the Rockefeller Foundation, and had subsequently won fame as a result of the discovery of Peking Man. Dr Davidson Black had been placed in charge of a special institute devoted to research into fossil man in China. At this institute, experts from Europe and America worked side by side with Chinese scholars in a unique community sustained by a spirit of research and discovery. Distinguished explorers like Sven Hedin, and American and French scholars all derived great benefit from this research centre. Indeed, who would not have been captivated by an exchange of views with Teilhard and Black? Both possessed the kind of magnetic attraction which characterizes men of genius. I, too, felt drawn into the orbit of their personalities and interests, and could have wished for nothing better than an opportunity to work with them.

The immediate occasion for my doing so was a letter which Dr Black wrote me from Peking on 13 March 1934. Quite apart from the significance which it held for me personally, I should like to reproduce it here in extract form, since it may serve as a documentary record of the research into Asian prehistory which so fascinated Teilhard.

> I am tremendously interested in the work you have been doing because it has such a very vital bearing on the problems of the Cenozoic confronting us. Your news of the Late Tertiary rising of the plateau is splendid and fits in with what we are now able to

surmise to have been the history of the northeastern part of Asia. . . . I planned to begin next year with funds derived from America taking to India for a short time some of our own men knowing the Cenozoic problem of the Far East and working as a part of the G.S.I. under their auspices and publishing in their journals. Alas, the depression in the U.S.A. has effectually put a stop to my dream. Now since you are working in the same field, I am simply delighted and I do hope you will be able to continue the work with adequate support for some years. . . Fossil Primates and possibly early Hominids are probable in the region and the general sequence of fossil fauna and flora and stratigraphy would add greatly to the post-Pontian history that is so badly needed. If you can forward this idea in connection with any plans you now have, please do so, for it would be greatly to the advantage of all interested in Cenozoic research if you could carry it on for as many years as you can devote to it. My original plan called for an extension of work into Baluchistan and along the east borders of Persia, where I went in 1932 . . . I should be greatly obliged if you would let me have reprints of the various papers to be published by you and the other men and collaborators of your expedition, and I shall see that all our papers reach you as soon as they appear.

With best wishes from Grabau, Teilhard and myself . . .

In a postscript, he wrote:

It would be simply splendid if you could continue on in South Asia, and we could exchange ideas and get you to come to Peking when you have a bit of spare time.

While I was gratified that my plans had been co-ordinated with those of the Peking Institute, what particularly pleased me about this letter was its allusion to a visit to Peking. Dr Black had undoubtedly discussed the plans mentioned in his letter with Teilhard, and it was this thought which prompted me to write to him at once and invite him to join my projected expedition to Northern India. Teilhard did not keep me waiting long for a reply to my invitation, which he enthusiastically accepted, promising to meet me in India in the autumn of 1935.

If I say all this by way of introduction, it is only to convey the sense of anticipation with which I awaited Teilhard's arrival in Kashmir in September 1935. I had preserved a vivid recollection of his striking face and dark, penetrating gaze ever since our first encounter, and looked forward to his arrival in the happy expectation of great experiences and events to come. First, however, I proposed to introduce him to the way in which I had employed chronological occurrences during the glaciation of the Kashmir Himalayas as a guide to the age of certain palaeolithic cultures which I had discovered in the foothills of the Soan Valley during the spring. Where such relationships between Ice Age and prehistory were concerned, Teilhard's area of research in China had nothing of comparable value to offer.

Leaving France at the beginning of September, he travelled by sea to Bombay, where he wrote a letter dated 23 September:[1]

[1] *Letters from a Traveller*, New York, Harper, 1962, p. 210.

> Bombay is a big, white and rather commonplace city, surrounded by sea. The spur of the headland is occupied by luxurious Anglo-Hindu buildings. Over the rest sprawls the huddle of the native town, a teeming medley of dark Hindu and Semitic types. What I like best is the great bushy trees with red and yellow flowers, through which from time to time you see the flight of flocks of green parrots. The monsoon is just over but it is still humid and already hot. It will be better in the north.
>
> I had a very kind welcome here from the Spanish Fathers at St Xavier's College. . . . I have finished my business in Bombay and am taking the train for the north this evening—the 'frontier mail'—which should get me tomorrow evening to Rawalpindi (Punjab) where I shall be met by Paterson, the Englishman. From there we leave together the next day to join de Terra in Srinagar (Kashmir).

In accordance with my instructions, the British archaeologist T. T. Paterson, a member of my expedition, met Teilhard at Rawalpindi by car. From there they drove to Kashmir, where I greeted Teilhard at Srinagar. He was somewhat amused to see the headquarters of my expedition—a houseboat which I was sharing with my wife and small daughter—but, whatever reservations he may have had about my romantic abode, nothing of them was detectable in his gracious manner. Watching him as he sat at table, clad in khaki drill and chatting like a man of the world, I should never have taken him for a priest.

Next day we were able to make a tour in Paterson's company. I must confess that, all in all, we made a pretty strange team. Paterson had recently completed his archaeological studies at Cambridge. It was obvious that he was determined to win his spurs on this expedition, which he did, thanks to his vitality and intelligence. His sonorous English betrayed his Scottish origins, which also found expression in the drily humorous remarks which punctuated his conversation from time to time. Just as Teilhard spoke English with a French accent, so my own accent testified to my German origins, but this did nothing to impair the harmony of our scientific discussions on glacier tracks or mammoth-bones.

I remember that both Paterson and I plied our guest with data and explanations in order to elicit his comments. It was always hard to wrest Teilhard away from a promising geological discovery before he had exhausted all its possible interpretations. In so doing, he invariably devised certain criteria of whose validity he had first to be thoroughly convinced. Only then would his thoughts turn to wider implications, and, before one knew it, he had given his listeners an entirely new view of things. He had a brilliant capacity for proceeding straight to a synthesis from carefully sifted details.

During a tour of one of the Himalayan valleys, where the caravan route to Tibet and China begins, he recalled the great French expedition to Central Asia which subsequently passed into the annals of Asian exploration under the name of '*la Croisière jaune*', and in which he had taken part. The motorized party had left Kashmir in 1931 and crossed the Pamirs into Chinese Turkestan under the leadership of Georges-Marie Haardt, whom Teilhard waited for in Aksu. This was how, after our excursion in October, he came to write to the widow of the leader of the expedition:

> I am sure that on seeing this address you will be touched to hear how vividly this country-side reminds me of the expedition. I can see the marks of caterpillar-tracks on the mountain passes, and memories of Georges-Marie—that is, really of you—seldom if ever desert me. How time flies, but how vivid events remain! This corner of Asia is full of the relics of such endeavours to conquer the world. And the expedition was one of those ventures which set their sights a little higher each time. I don't need to describe Kashmir to you, because you know it: a green river valley framed by two snowy ranges. The weather is superb, the rice-fields quite yellow. At the first breath of autumn the huge plane-trees begin to turn red. On the edge of the fragrant forests, beturbanned peasants gather walnuts near orchards full of red apples. It looks like a reflection of Aksu, where I waited for the party at the same time of year. . . .
>
> I arrived at Srinagar a week ago and shall be travelling down to Rawalpindi tomorrow with my companions, de Terra of Yale University and Paterson, a young man from Cambridge. I am most anxious to understand Kashmir's geology, which is the key to the geology of the Himalayan foothills, where I shall mainly be working. Quite apart from that, I am utterly enchanted by my encounter with the mountains. According to one plan, though it is not entirely settled yet, we shall tour around to the south and east of Rawalpindi. Later on I shall

probably go to Simla. The hot season is almost over in Northern India. All in all, I arrived here just at the right moment. . . .

In the Sind Valley, where we made our excursion, we met pony caravans which had carried woollen and felt rugs across the highest mountain passes in the world. With their turbans, bearded faces and long caftan-like robes, the drivers resembled oriental pilgrims of the sort depicted in Persian miniatures.

A letter which Teilhard wrote to his friends Simone and Max Bégouën on 5 November contains a very typical sketch of Kashmir:

My last letter to you was written from Bombay. Since that time I've been very much on the move, though always in the same corner of India. First a week in the magnificent setting of Kashmir, as an introduction under de Terra's guidance to the Himalayan glacial formations: huge snow-covered masses, with a border of pine-forest overlooking a valley rich in green vegetation; on the roads I could see the tracks of Haardt's caterpillars, still perfectly fresh. Grey mud villages in which the turbanned and moustached peasants live and say their prayers in the mosques, with their womenfolk, always cowed-looking and generally ragged, with a ring in the left nostril. Camels, cows and buffaloes are perpetually across the road and you have to look out for them: overhead, a dazzling light and a permanently cloudless sky. Now that the weather's not so hot, it's ideal country for the geologist.

On the whole I'm well pleased with our work. For the Pliocene and Pleistocene in Asia, I couldn't

> imagine a grander complement to China, and de Terra is the perfect guide (He has already done the Pamirs and Karakoram twice.) . . .[2]

Our excursion into the Sind Valley, where Teilhard spotted traces of the Citroën-Haardt expedition, gave him a chance to inspect a neolithic settlement which Paterson had discovered there. He told us that the geometrical patterns on the ancient potsherds bore a certain resemblance to similar pieces which he had seen in the Gobi Desert. This led to a discussion on pottery and the keeping of domestic animals, which are regarded as marking the beginning of the neolithic period. Kashmir, we reflected, abutted on the highlands of Iran and Afghanistan, where the neolithic cultures were supposed to have originated. On the mountain slopes above our valley were wild sheep and goats whose ancestors might have provided the basis for a first attempt at livestock-breeding in the neolithic period. Nor was it entirely beyond the bounds of possibility that wild grasses had existed there from whose seeds man ground the first flour to make bread. Ideas like these helped to transport us into the period which Teilhard described as the vital era of 'socialization', during which hunters' and food-gatherers' cultures evolved into sedentary, organized communities.[3]

What prompted us to discuss such questions further was a visit to a prehistoric monument not far from the mouth of the Sind Valley, where I had done a certain amount of digging shortly before Teilhard's arrival. The site in question boasted a group of isolated, plate-shaped

[2] *Letters from a Traveller*, pp. 213-14.
[3] *The Phenomenon of Man*, New York, Harper, 1959, pp. 203-5.

boulders, up to twelve feet in height, which had immediately reminded me, during my first visit, of the sort of ancient monument that occurs at Stonehenge and in Brittany, the so-called megaliths or menhirs. These huge, mossy, weather-beaten stones, which stood on a hill overlooking the entire Vale of Kashmir, seemed to endow the age-old monument with a special solemnity. The site appeared to have been a temple precinct, possibly associated with sun-worship.[4] When I showed Teilhard the polished stone axes, pestles, mortars and pottery adorned with matting imprints which I had found in the deepest layers of the digging, conversation at once returned to the great upheavals that had occurred during the neolithic period. The fact that no metal objects of any kind had come to light during my excavation of the temple precinct seemed to indicate that it dated from the latter part of the Stone Age, a circumstance which led Teilhard to speak of the way in which archaeologists currently working in Asia had neglected research into that period. Why, he asked, should people neglect the very period which had witnessed such a marked upsurge in the evolution of man? It was easier to sympathize with such an oversight in the case of India because archaeologists had been focussing their attention on the Indus Valley culture of the 3rd millenium B.C. Excavations at Mohenjo-Daro in Sind Province and at Harrappa in the Punjab had disclosed the real foundations of Indian history, which antedated the influx of Indo-European peoples by approximately fifteen hundred years. It was only when I read Teilhard's chapter on

[4] I later published the results of these excavations in *Proceedings, Am. Phil. Soc.*, Vol. 85, 1942, pp. 483-504.

'The Neolithic Metamorphosis'[5] that I realized why, when visiting what was probably the earliest religious monument in India, he had spoken so sharply and impatiently about the gaps in our knowledge of the neolithic period. His impatience was that of a scientist obsessed with spiritual questions and eager to grasp the underlying meaning of history. One cannot but join him in deploring such a lacuna in our knowledge of a period 'geologically negligible, but long enough nevertheless for the selection and domestication of all the animals and plants on which we are still living today. . . . In a matter of ten or twenty thousand years man divided up the earth and struck his roots in it.'

In the interval since Teilhard pondered and recorded his ideas on the vast process in the course of which man took possession of the earth and technically exploited it for the first time, archaeological research has made great strides, particularly in Asia. Working in the area between the Caspian and Mesopotamia, American archaeologists like Carlton S. Coon and Robert J. Braidwood have elicited new information which is of vital importance to our understanding of the neolithic period. By using the radio-carbon method we can, for instance, ascertain that domestic animals, e.g. dogs, were first kept beside the Caspian in about 9000 B.C., and that the earliest-known permanent settlements in Iraq date from about the same period. Similarly, the results of research made available to me have enabled me to establish that pottery first originated in the Iranian highlands in the first half of the 6th century B.C. Increased accuracy in identifying

[5] *The Phenomenon of Man*, p. 203 et seq.

dates of origin has made the organization of sedentary man less mysterious than it once appeared to Teilhard. It should be mentioned, in this respect, that the all too brief section of Teilhard's book which deals with these questions makes no reference to the environmental factors which may have influenced and even stimulated this re-ordering of human life. The coincidence of plant-cultivation and stock-breeding with the general climatic improvement ushered in by the post-glacial period was particularly marked in these highlands. Consequently, if there was a sudden transition from consciousness to the exploitation of the generative powers of flora and fauna at this particular stage, it is likely that this occurrence was connected with ecological factors. Anyone who overlooks this must, of necessity, attribute the development of consciousness to psychical forces about whose nature science is wholly incapable of supplying precise information. In a later chapter I shall have occasion to say more about Teilhard's patent neglect of environmental factors in the evolutionary process. It is conceivable, of course, that when writing about this subject in Peking he was without the requisite specialized literature, which has been substantially augmented since then by more recent research.

Although Teilhard regarded the neolithic metamorphosis as a world-wide phenomenon, one cannot concur with his assertion that it affected the Old and New Worlds more or less simultaneously. This is belied by the dissimilarity of domestic animals and cereals in America and Eurasia. In the same way, the fact that technical discoveries such as the alloying of metals and the invention of the wheel occurred much later in the

New World leads one to infer the existence of a long interval between the evolution of the earliest cultures there and in the Old World. Although controversy still surrounds the subject of autochthonous American cultures, good reasons can be adduced for supposing that trans-Pacific migrations took place, and these furnish no evidence of a simultaneous and world-wide differentiation of consciousness. It is equally erroneous to connect man's first appearance in America with the neolithic period, for mammoth-hunters probably traversed the Bering Straits from Asia toward the close of the Ice Age, or thirty thousand years ago. For these reasons, a 'collective' consciousness in Teilhard's sense cannot have become diffused throughout the world simultaneously, but by stages and with large regional time-differences. Consciousness can better be likened to a ladder whose rungs point in different directions and came into being at very different times. Asian and American ethnology provides sufficient examples of this, relics of age-old traditions which date back to the Stone Age and can still be studied in a few remote places today.

Given Teilhard's broad view of things, however, such differences in the evolution of early civilizations can in no way be regarded as arguments against his theory of a break-through in human intelligence during the neolithic period. According to this, ethnic grouping signifies the commencement of a new and still continuing process in which man's exploitation of natural forces has progressed from the planting of seed-corn to the exploration of outer space. Easy as it may seem to level criticism at Teilhard's individual ideas, this should not encourage us to lose sight of their grand design. While still on the subject of our days in Kashmir, I should add that I noticed, even at that stage, how very difficult it was to pursue a discussion with Teilhard about factual observations. Even at such times he would only go as far as seemed justified by other considerations, giving the impression that he was holding back something which he preferred to reserve for a special occasion. One could, however, gain an idea of his train of thought from the odd *bon mot* which he uttered, and such an instance arose during our trip from Kashmir into the neighbouring lowlands.

We were driving down into the plain from Srinagar in a heavily laden car. The road ran above the roaring river, faithfully following its convolutions at a dizzy height. We might easily have plunged into the raging torrent beneath if our chauffeur had not been compelled to drive cautiously on account of the numerous cows and buffaloes which trotted casually along the road. We had to avoid them with care because to have maimed or killed one of these sacred beasts would unquestionably have meant a spell in jail. Even the monkeys which are so common in the forests of Kashmir were considered sacred in this part of the country. The notion that it would be impossible to capture a monkey without breaking the law prompted Teilhard to remark that, in that case, we should have to confine ourselves to collecting fossil apes.

Our route to Rawalpindi took us across the deep gorge cut by the Jhelum, referred to in Herodotus' *History* as the Hydaspes, on whose lower reaches Alexander the Great fought his first and only battle in India. Our car passed a continual succession of geological formations, some of which we stopped to examine so that I could explain individual features to Teilhard. As far as our rate of progress allowed, it was here that he absorbed his first impressions of the geological history of the range bordering the immense mountain system with whose northern extremities he had become acquainted in Central Asia. He was particularly fascinated by the stratigraphy of the valley walls, whose complex folds bore witness to the great convulsions that had attended the formation of the mountains. Comparison of individual phases with those of China was important to him in that it supplied him with information about the geological conditions which must have affected the evolution of man at the close of the Ice Age and the beginning of the Tertiary epoch. There were moments when we felt ourselves transported back in time to those far-off days when the youthful Himalayas were mantled with tropical forests in which, over millions of years, primates related to man advanced slowly toward the event regarded by Teilhard as the most important outcome of organic evolution: the birth of consciousness.

II

During the autumn of 1935 we transferred our base of operations from idyllic Kashmir to the foothills of the Himalayas. Here, mountain streams referred to by the chroniclers of Alexander the Great flow across broad, barren plains which convey a feeling of remoteness and desolation. To the south, like some geological ruin, rose the Salt Range, our next objective, whose rock formations we planned to comb for fossils from the period immediately prior to the Ice Age.

Teilhard and I left Rawalpindi on 9 October, travelling in a small truck accompanied by an Indian assistant, a cook and a camp servant. The only vehicle I had been able to hire for this tour was so decrepit that it got stuck in the first dry river-bed we came to. Teilhard jumped out with a laugh and heaved with the rest, and from that moment onwards I knew he would share all our discomforts unhesitatingly. This thought dispelled any apprehensions I may have felt about the improvised nature of the trip, which had necessitated my making a minor change of plan at Teilhard's request.

I could set out to describe any one of the days we spent collecting fossils in the brightly coloured ravines, but time has fused the details into a blur of mental images. I should like to draw on these in order to portray Teilhard as I remember him in that desolate and geologically dramatic region. He fitted so well into the wilderness. The desert has always aroused the ascetic in man and stimulated the spiritual and visionary sides of his nature, which is probably why men of destiny like Christ and Mohammed experienced moments of spiritual exaltation there.

I remember days which began as the sun sucked up the milky shroud of morning mist in the valleys, days of which each seemed like a new feat of creation performed to the ticking of some vast geological clock. The flawless sky resembled a glass dome. Stones and shrubs quivered in the noonday heat. The rugged landscape looked like a wind-lashed sea composed of ravines and ridges, an endless succession of carmine, yellow, grey and violet rock formations that seemed to have sprung from an inexhaustible palette. A river fed by the waters of the Himalayas wound its devious way toward the embrace of the Indus and the Arabian Gulf, gnawing at the base of crags which had been millions of years in the making. Among the rocks, time stood still and life slept its geological sleep. Fossil bones and petrified imprints of palm-leaves lay embedded in stone like hieroglyphs which had to be deciphered if we were to follow the evolution of life. The skeletal remains of gazelles, wild horses, mastodons and, last but not least, anthropoid apes all helped to shed light on the problem of man's origins.

Teilhard stood beside me in khaki trousers and open-necked shirt, his face under its pith helmet wearing the impatient look of one who is on the track of great things. All at once, he started off up the mountain-side, threading his way through a flock of grazing goats. Noticing that his feet were shod in light tennis-shoes, I warned him to look out for poisonous snakes, which were particularly numerous in the area. He glanced back at me in surprise and said that he could feel the ground much better in light shoes. Then he scrambled up the hill, nimble as a dancer, and vanished among the goats. The goatherds' occasional calls ensured that we maintained contact in the barren wilderness. Old men and boys appeared from nowhere and joined us for a while. We met one toothless old greybeard who was anxious to guide us to a place where, he said, there were large fossil bones. Teilhard was busy with a fossil tooth, however, and betrayed not the slightest interest in this tempting piece of information. He sat down on a rock, produced his notebook from his pocket and began to write.

It was Teilhard's custom to record his observations in the form of rough sketches which usually depicted a stratigraphic sequence and bore a note of its geographical location, as far as it was possible to identify this from the map. For all that, he only used map references for purposes of general orientation, since he had his own ideas about each geological situation. I very soon realized that his unique blend of knowledge and intuition endowed his scientific observations with such an individual and authoritative quality that a geological map seemed veritably antiquated by comparison.

On 16 October he described his impressions as follows:

> De Terra and I . . . have been wandering about the Salt Range, sometimes by camel, sometimes by car, sometimes under canvas, and sometimes (as today) in one of the comfortable bungalows that the British government has put up at frequent intervals for the convenience of travelling sahibs. You arrive; the caretaker opens the bungalow and you move in and install yourself with your kit and your boys. My boy is called Simon; he has a big turban, a formidable moustache and makes an excellent *housemaid.* A very convenient arrangement.
>
> It's a picturesque country, but three-parts desert, cracked and stony. There are moments when I might be back in Egypt or Abyssinia. All the plants and trees are thorny. I am extremely well and surprised to find myself so 'young'. Every day we are on our feet nearly all day long, and I feel no tiredness at all. Not a cloud in the sky: we wear nothing but slacks and a shirt—very convenient.[1]

[1] *Letters from a Traveller*, p. 212.

A few days later he wrote to his friend Abbé Breuil in Paris:

> In every direction the ground is furrowed by erosion, and the fields the people cultivate are poor and stony. . . . The population is entirely Moslem. I should like you to see the women here so that you could appreciate what our western civilization has succeeded in winning for their sisters in Europe. The poor creatures here are permanently cowed, prematurely lined and buried in their veils. All this has got to be swept away, and before very long too.
>
> I am yielding to the exotic charm of the place, with less enthusiasm than before, to be sure, but still just as fully; and I never tire of the pleasure of seeing the charming little chipmunks coming to nibble titbits at my door, or the flocks of parrots bickering in the trees—these parrots fly at a surprising speed and never stop their chatter, whether in the air or among the branches. We are staying in Rawalpindi for a few more days, using it as a centre for drives into the countryside. I am proposing to go farther east in November, towards Simla.

Teilhard's eyes were everywhere. He felt so at home in the open air that he could enjoy Nature as only those who have studied the evolution of life from the ground upwards can.

He was extremely excited to see the places in the Soan Valley where I had found Stone-Age artefacts some months earlier. We spent several days collecting tools which palaeolithic man had fashioned from splinters of rock. These we found in old river-beds high above the valley, axes, scrapers and countless splinters which proved that the raw material had been shaped on the spot. Teilhard was always stooping to pick up a new stone and examine it critically for signs of human handiwork. When a contented '*c'est bon*' escaped his lips, we could be certain that it was an artefact. The manner in which he weighed different criteria one against the other proved him to be adept in prehistoric research. It was from him that I learnt the rudiments of palaeolithic typology, which stood me in good stead in later years. Teilhard had all the enthusiasm of a detective who is permanently aware of his responsibility to some higher authority. There was a restlessness about him, as though he were determined to deduce the leit-motiv of human evolution and the impulse of psychical energy toward fuller consciousness from geological occurrences. The idea that we were dealing with documentary records left by a primeval intellect which, to judge from its geographical location, belonged to two distinct cultures, evoked graphic images. Teilhard was not unique in his ability to understand the prehistoric world, but it was so strong in his case that he could literally put himself in the place of primitive man. His powers of memory were such that he could describe and sketch the precise shape of artefacts which he had found in China ten years before.

In this way, the barren wilderness became filled with life. Stone tools became gauges of human intellect, layers of clay were transformed into the dust-storms which still leave deposits in the same area today, and fossil bones turned into elephants and herds of buffalo. We reversed the course of human history and turned back the geological clock, believing that we could thereby trace the progress made by the human intellect since those primeval times. The history of civilization cannot summon up immense vistas like these, but Teilhard had the gift of seeing human evolution in all-embracing geological perspective.

After our excursion to the Salt Range, I took Teilhard to see evidence of early geological upheavals in the gravel formations at the foot of the Kashmir Himalayas. While there, we came upon a place where the strata exposed by an Ice-Age river had been folded by intense pressure. The question at once arose as to whether primitive man had actually witnessed the Himalayas' last uplift, and we had to search the strata for artefacts in order to settle the point.

This was easier said than done. We were surrounded by a vast tract of bare hill and plain, devoid of proper paths. A hired car took us as far as Jammu, then the winter residence of the ruling prince of Kashmir and Jammu, where we stayed in a bungalow. The caretaker surprised us by producing a list of beverages such as only the pampered taste of British colonial administrators could have devised. We drank a bottle of claret together, and had just finished supper when my Indian assistant came in. He never shared his meals with us because, as a member of the Brahmin caste, he was not permitted to. When Teilhard first heard of this peculiar custom he exclaimed that no mortal had the right to consider a fellow-man so impure that he would not share a meal with him on religious grounds. The caste system hung over India like a nightmare shadow which even Gandhi's great subsequent feats have failed to dispel entirely. 'So far as I have been able to form an opinion of them,' Teilhard wrote later, 'the Hindus have been a disappointment to me. In them, too, creative power seems to be in a pretty poor way, and you have to go to India to appreciate the numbing and deadening effect of a religion obsessed by ritualism and outward form.'

How could he, to whom freedom of intellectual development was of such prime importance, have formed any other conclusion? It could have meant little to him when our Brahmin related that evening how he had visited a Hindu temple famed for its phallic symbols. Apparently, the steps leading to this shrine consisted of limestone which was full of fossils resembling the creative emblem of the god Siva. I had already noticed in Kashmir that Teilhard had little sympathy for the erotic art-forms of ancient India, particularly when they were associated with a variety of animal shapes. In his eyes, this art recalled the long-dead era when human superstition made a cult out of man's relationship with lower forms of life. Although I concede that an emphasis on such relationships can militate against a genuine awareness of man's calling, one of the distinguishing features of Hinduism is its belief in the cosmic unity of all life. This ancient Indian concept should not have been entirely alien to Teilhard, considering that he himself believed in an all-pervading psychical force. On the other hand, his idea of creative evolution in Nature differed from the Indian in that he regarded man as its end-product and ultimate goal, whereas the Hindu believes in man's reincarnation as an animal.

I had repeated occasion to admire Teilhard's persevering attempts to identify signs of primeval intelligence in the primitive stone tools which he discovered during our subsequent excursions into the barren, rocky wilderness. In view of the vast extent of these plains, few of whose valleys permitted of thorough geological examination, it was hard for us to find proof of the geological age of artefacts belonging to the Middle Quaternary, at which stage the Himalayas experienced a particularly strong uplift. Teilhard deserves the credit for having elicited this proof. I was able to date the stones which he identified as primitive artefacts at the close of the second Himalayan glaciation, which put the 'proto-Soan' culture of Northern India roughly on a par, chronologically, with Peking Man.

Now that Indian prehistory had suddenly acquired a hypothetical relationship to the age of the earliest man in continental Asia, Teilhard was struck by a new idea. Was there, both in Asia and Europe, a geological horizon on which could be perceived the first glimmer of human intelligence? It was certainly remarkable that the earliest and most primitive artefacts in both China and India belonged to the Middle Quaternary, and that a similar boundary was discernible in the palaeolithic period in Europe. Following up this train of thought, we came to the mystery of anthropogenesis. Surrounded by the rocky wilderness, we debated as to whether these tools could really be regarded as the earliest records of human intelligence. Why shouldn't the first men have tried their hand with other materials—wood and bone, for instance? Although Peking Man had fashioned tools out of bone, it seemed unlikely that artefacts of wood or bone would have survived here for hundreds of millenia. In default of other information, stone tools would have to serve as the criteria of primeval intelligence.

Our observations had brought us to the point which

Teilhard describes in several of his works as the major geological key to the elucidation of man's origin. We had seen formations in the Salt Range containing fossil remains of anthropoid apes dating from the Late Tertiary. These layers were separated by a 'discordance' or stratal gap from the Ice-Age gravel which contained the palaeolithic tools, a gap symbolic of the period in which man must have appeared. When we drew a geological diagram of this, Teilhard remarked that he had never come across a more striking illustration of the problem of man's age. It must have been these observations in Northern India which prompted him to write, in one of his later works:[2]

> Between the last strata of the Pliocene age, in which man is absent, and the next, in which the geologist is dumbfounded to find the first chipped flints, what has happened? It is our task to divine and to measure the answers to these questions before we follow, step by step, the march of mankind right down to the decisive stage in which it is involved today.

The lacuna in our geological diagram demonstrated the period in which the 'transition' to human consciousness had taken place.

As I listened to Teilhard talking about this in the middle of the stony waste, I reflected what an historic spot it was from the palaeontologist's point of view. We were in the area where the origin of man had first been considered in geological perspective. In the year 1837 the Edinburgh-born doctor Hugh Falconer had reported finding the first fossil tooth of an anthropoid ape in a

[2] *The Phenomenon of Man*, p. 164.

stratigraphic sequence resembling those to which I had just introduced Teilhard. On the basis of rich deposits of fossils, Falconer had identified a number of vertebrates (the so-called Siwalik fauna). These displayed phylogenic affinities to still surviving forms of certain species which also play a part in Indian mythology, e.g. the giant tortoise and the monkey. These fossil remains, which dated from the Upper Tertiary, suggested to Falconer that man could be related to the course of geological evolution and might be roughly as old as the Siwalik fauna. Revolutionary by contemporary standards, his theory fell upon deaf ears because no one yet had any real idea of the existence of fossil man.

Great ideas arrive 'on doves' feet', as Nietzsche once said. They require a special climate of opinion before they can bear fruit. Leonardo da Vinci's geological theories were only developed by Charles Lyell in the 19th century, thus laying the foundations of modern geology. Although Teilhard's knowledge of natural history was generally excellent, I cannot recall that he ever showed any particular interest in the history of geology or prehistoric research, nor do his writings suggest that he did. One possible explanation is that he was too heavily committed to his own research and too eager to invest it with new meaning.

Our highly laborious quest for fossil remains of anthropoid apes calls to mind certain passages in Teilhard's book *Le Groupe zoölogique humain*, in which he speaks of the role played by the development of the primates in the general evolution of life. Where could we have found a better opportunity to investigate this important problem than in Northern India, where the mountainsides yield such fossils? Since Teilhard regarded the history of life as 'a stirring of consciousness veiled by morphology', his ideas on the culmination of this process among the primates may well have been enriched by these remains of fossil anthropoids. Their fossil traces appear almost simultaneously in the Upper Tertiary rock formations of three continents, and with a diversity such as no longer exists today. We can really speak, with the American palaeontologist G. G. Simpson, in terms of an 'explosive' evolutionary phase. My earlier fossil collections from Northern India had furnished fresh evidence of this sub-division among the higher primates, as a result of which the palaeontologists W. K. Gregory and M. Hellman were able to identify a closer relationship to man in some species than exists among surviving anthropoid types. The meagre numbers of fossil skulls and partial or complete skeletons found in Europe and Africa confirm such physiological approximations to man. While the development of the cranium approached human shape, the close of the Tertiary epoch saw the emergence of peculiar transitional forms (e.g. the Australopithecus group in South Africa) which were distinguished by man-like teeth and upright stance but whose skull-formation precludes our describing them as human beings proper. In India, as elsewhere, the Pliocene was dominated by a variety of land mammals —an animal society which seems so modern by comparison with the reptiles and amphibians of the preceding epoch that, as Teilhard said, one actually misses the presence of fireplaces tended by thinking creatures. A modern world, but devoid of consciousness, of the smoke of snug camp-fires, of tools and cave art! Yet, gradually taking shape amid this medley of ungulates and predators of all kinds was the refined nervous system of the higher primates, among whom consciousness could have emerged at any time.

Since cerebral development in the anthropoid group progressed in the direction of consciousness within the general framework of mammalian evolution, Teilhard was in accord with other experts in regarding this process as monophyletic, that is to say, confined to a single stock. He could not subscribe to a 'monogenetic' theory of man's ancestry (in Darwinian terms, descended from a single pair of ancestors) because there is little prospect of finding scientific evidence to support it. In his view, it should be enough for us that man is in the thick of the life-struggle and that, within life as a whole, he represents a unique and extreme manifestation of psychical energy. Human reasoning-power towers so phenomenally far above every other product of evolution that one might be forgiven for abandoning the quest for its actual point of departure, scientifically enthralling though the problem may be. Those who, like Teilhard, are disposed to regard anthropogenesis as an undemonstrable occurrence, are nevertheless bound to envisage some form of special mutation which must have come about in accordance with the general law of species-development, a 'mutation unique of its kind' in so far as the resultant human race exhibits peculiar biological characteristics such as Teilhard discusses exhaustively in his writings.[3] True, every mutation is unique, but in terms of Teilhard's conception of man's origins it appears as the fulfilment

[3] *Le Groupe zoölogique humain*, Éditions Albin Michel, Paris 1956, pp. 81, 92 et seq.

of a very special trend in organic evolution, the trend toward the development of consciousness. In this sense, mutation should be regarded as a leap forward in creative evolution based, to some extent, on a 'quantum' emission of vital energy among the primates.

This determinist interpretation of the origin of man also explains why Teilhard bestowed such scant attention on environmental factors. How could an internally governed evolution have been influenced by climatic changes (and by the primates' consequent change of diet)? It was consistent with Teilhard's theory of a neolithic metamorphosis that he disregarded ecological factors. It may be objected that we know nothing of the environmental pressures to which the anthropoids were subjected, but that should not deter a scientist from taking them into account. Indeed, the Indian fossils prompted some experts to regard the geologically late raising of the Himalayas as having given anthropogenesis a special biological stimulus, a theory which I had already dismissed as untenable on the basis of earlier geological research. I felt far more inclined, in 1937, to adduce another factor, namely, the geologically demonstrable shifting of climatic belts toward the close of the Pliocene, to account for the decisive changes in fauna and stratum-formation which undoubtedly influenced the evolution of the higher primates.[4] It is

[4] See my contribution to the symposium on *Early Man* which took place at Philadelphia in 1937, on which occasion Teilhard delivered a lecture on his research in China. (George G. McCurdy, *Early Man*, Lippincott, Philadelphia 1937.) The results of my research in India are fully described in another of my works: *The Ice Age in India and Associated Human Cultures*, Carnegie Institution of Washington D.C., Publ. No. 493, 1939, 354 pp.

widely known that mutations can be accelerated by critical environmental conditions, just as, more than a century ago, Darwin and Wallace ascertained the influence of geographical factors on the natural selection of the species. After examining all available information about this climatic change in the northern hemisphere, a geologist will recognize the existence of a critical situation which no one who tackles the problems posed by the origin of man should overlook. If there was, in Teilhard's sense, a psychogenesis which evolved from general biogenetic processes, I find it hard to believe that it was not influenced by changes in environment. Not to have given sufficient weight to such factors must be regarded as one of the weakest points in Teilhard's magnificent edifice of ideas.

In order to appreciate this, one must remember the great climatic event which impinged, to a greater or lesser extent, upon all forms of terrestrial life: the Ice Age. Not only did glaciers move out of the mountain ranges into adjoining lowlands and large areas of Europe and North America turn into frozen wastes, but a general displacement of climatic zones took place. Lakes and verdant plains inhabited by herds of elephants, buffaloes and deer appeared in the deserts of Africa, Asia and America. The first men lived in different surroundings, in a world which was in many places better stocked with animals and, in the temperate zones, colder than it is today. What was the explanation of the Ice Age, and in what way may it have influenced anthropogenesis? The British astronomer Fred Hoyle has pointed to the changes in solar radiation which occur during the solar system's passage through space. On this basis, the glacial periods were brought about by cosmic processes, an explanation which gains credence from the fact that five distinct glacial periods can be identified in the geological formations of the past 900 million years. We have not yet discovered, of course, how far early climatic changes influenced the evolution of life. In the case of the last glacial period, it is conceivable that changes in solar radiation had a bearing on the accelerated development of the primates' brain. It is strange that Teilhard makes no mention of such relationships between the Ice Age and anthropogenesis. Since I shall be returning to his ideas on the origin of man in a later chapter, I will only say here that in India he was mainly preoccupied with understanding those geological processes which are connected with the origin of man.

There were moments when he felt within arm's length of early man in India, as, for instance, on the day when we found a layer beside the Indus filled with fossil bones. They were so easy to collect that we filled three packing-cases with them in a single day.[5] Although these fossils were somewhat older than the fauna found with Peking Man, Teilhard secretly hoped that the site would yield remains of higher primates, perhaps even of men. I distinctly remember the suppressed excitement with which he worked on the site all that day. When the fiery sun sank behind a dust-cloud and the hoped-for trophy had not materialized, Teilhard did not, contrary to expectation, appear disappointed. His confidence

[5] On 13 July 1936 Teilhard wrote to Dr W. Granger, palaeontologist at the American Museum of Natural History in New York, telling him that he had despatched to the Museum from Peking three cases of prepared fossils which 'were found in the upper Siwalik strata by de Terra and myself.'

that future research would clarify the problem of anthropogenesis was unshakable. On 15 November 1955 he wrote from Rawalpindi:[6]

> . . . For the past three weeks there has not been much change in my life in India: long days, full of interest, spent in the sub-Himalayan hills—millions of yards of consolidated mud and gravel creased like crêpe paper. We're beginning to see our way to clarifying our findings. A week in the neighbourhood of the Indus brought us a respectable pile of cases of fossils found in a new district. On the whole I feel that we have done well. Once again Providence will be found to have led me to a critical point at just the psychological moment. I do indeed believe that it is the work in which I'm now sharing that will lay the first serious foundation for the prehistory of India. The weather at present is marvellous. Yesterday in particular, when we were working in the jagged ravines of a minor mountain range south of here, the setting was tremendous. In the foreground, deep crevasses exposing under the mimosa growth the striped mass (yellow, violet, pink) of the regularly curved Pleistocene formations; in the middle distance, much further back, the violet mass of Pliocene and Miocene mud almost forming one with the great chains; and finally, floating in the blue sky on the horizon, the white barrier of the Pir Panjal, the last corner of the Himalayan peaks; and lying over the whole scene a golden light playing on the dry, bleached grasses.

Teilhard was in his element here. Bathed in gold,

[6] *Letters from a Traveller*, pp. 215-16

the broad expanses at the foot of the highest mountain range in the world conjured up visions of the origin of man. Teilhard was fascinated anew by thoughts of man's past history, quite contrary to his expectations, considering that during the outward voyage to India he had written on 8 September:[7]

> It is almost as though, for reasons arising from the progress of my own science, the past and its discovery had ceased to interest me. *The past has revealed to me how the future is built*, and preoccupation with the future tends to sweep everything else aside. It is precisely that I may be able to speak with authority about the future that it is essential for me to establish myself more firmly than before as a specialist on the past. But isn't it an odd thing that the very object of my work should fade into the background as it yields me its fruits? and that I should attribute less value to the discoveries I may make because henceforward their interest for me has been superseded? Now that the fundamental discovery has been made, that we are carried along by an advancing wave of consciousness, does anything of importance remain to be disclosed in what has been left behind us? Certain rhythms or impulses, perhaps, that are still hidden from us by the slenderness of our knowledge at this actual moment. It is along these lines that I wish to do my thinking, and so save, if possible, the passion for geology for my old age. Even so, what a difference there is, in the object of my ambitions, between this voyage and the 1923 one! I hope I am right in looking on it as an advance.

[7] *Letters from a Traveller*, pp. 207-8.

But, although Teilhard's was really an intellectual passion and a great vocation, his friends could have predicted that India would be just the place to provide him with renewed incentives for research. His letters from there certainly confirm this, as did the enthusiasm which filled him while we were together.

III

Although it would have been in the interests of our studies to spend the winter in Northern India, this plan proved impracticable. In the first place, prolonging our stay would have meant procuring additional research equipment, which was not so easy to come by, and, secondly, Teilhard had fixed his departure for the end of December because he intended to move on to Java to familiarize himself with the latest discoveries of fossil men. The question now was, how to use our remaining weeks to best advantage. Teilhard was fascinated by the thought that no one had yet discovered any human fossils in Hindustan comparable in importance with Peking or Java Man. Our discussions of this problem frequently returned to the Narbada Valley in Central India, where an English archaeologist had found fossil vertebrates which pointed to the existence of a fauna apparently related to Java Man. There had even been reports of a fossil human skull found in that area which had been sent to a museum and subsequently mislaid. Although it was not very likely that we would come across such a precious trophy during a brief visit to Central India, we nonetheless hoped that we should be able to make some contribution to the problem of the dissemination of palaeolithic cultures in Southern Asia, thereby gaining a fresh idea of the geological boundaries within which the first men appeared on the periphery of Asia. Since Paterson had meanwhile told us of some interesting Stone-Age finds in the lower Indus Valley, we decided to visit his sites first, especially as they were not far from the famous ruined city of Mohenjo-Daro, where India's earliest civilization had been unearthed.

On 7 November, Teilhard and I took the train from Lahore to the lower reaches of the Indus. As the train rumbled slowly across the long bridge spanning the Sutlej, we thought of the Tibetan plateau where, more than 16,000 feet up, the giant river starts its headlong journey through the Himalayan gorges to the Indus. It was on the edge of the Tibetan plateau, over a century before, that the British palaeontologist Dr Hugh Falconer had reported finding the first relics of fossil anthropoid apes. No further investigations having been carried out in that inaccessible region since Falconer's time, Teilhard's friend and associate, Dr Davidson Black, cherished the idea of collecting fossils there. What prompted him was the thought that, not long before the onset of the glacial period, the Tibetan plateau lay at a much lower altitude and must therefore have formed part of the environment of the Siwalik fauna. I myself had made some contribution to this problem by finding indications of a very recent raising of the entire Himalayan range in Kashmir and Western Tibet. Teilhard would undoubtedly have followed up Dr Black's plans if they had ever been put into effect. Meanwhile, gazing down at the broad river from our compartment, we feasted our eyes for a while on the vast panorama which furnished such an impressive illustration of the geological dynamism of the Himalayas.

Towards morning, the cool fragrance of palm-tree oases crept into our compartment. A Moslem passenger had just spread out his prayer-mat. Before sinking to his knees in prayer he turned and asked us in broken English if his mat were facing in the direction of Mecca. Teilhard had just given the beturbanned old man a friendly nod of assent when the express entered a long curve, making it impossible for us to know for some moments whether our devout fellow-passenger was facing the right way or not.

Rays of light pierced the dawn sky outside, and then, suddenly, the wide expanse of the Indus hove into view, fishing-boats among the sand-banks and gleaming white houses scattered along the shore. This was Sukkur, a flourishing town set in the midst of an oasis. The morning light steeped the mud huts and palm-trees in delicate shades of pink and pale green, and behind them the greyish-yellow surface of the Sind Desert shimmered with the lustre of ancient glass. The rust-brown sails of the fishing-boats billowed in the morning breeze, soon to be filled by the sea-wind and borne down to the port of Karachi. The landscape reminded Teilhard so vividly of the Nile Valley and of Cairo, where he had worked as a teacher, that he felt as though he had been suddenly transported to Egypt. Here, as there, rivers threaded the desert with the luxuriant valley pastures to which the ancient civilizations had owed their wealth—yet how different had been their respective fates! While a great centre of civilization had existed in the Nile Valley for thousands of years and wielded influence over other cultures, the Indus Valley civilization had succumbed to invasion by alien peoples after roughly a thousand years. Here on the Indus, too, the mighty surge of political ambition which brought Alexander the Great to the western borders of India had ebbed. The former pupil of Aristotle abandoned the lower reaches of the Indus and set off for Babylonia once more without leaving any permanent mark, either personally or through the administrators of his oriental heritage, on India's culture or political structure. Even though certain Greek traditions are discernible in the art of North-West India, the great religions of Buddhism and Hinduism remained untouched by them. How limited the historical role of power-political ventures seems when compared with the rapid spread of the Indian, Jewish and Christian religions, as, vehicles of spiritual yearning, they advanced across whole continents from the Ganges Valley and Palestine. I cannot recall whether we actually spoke of such things after our daily wanderings on the outskirts of the desert, but, in view of the impressions that follow, it seems highly probable.

The air about us hummed with the noise of machinery, lorries and columns of labourers engaged on the construction of a great dam which was to irrigate an area the size of England with the waters of the Indus. The future, which Teilhard's personal view of history prompted him to conceive of as growing consciousness, here found expression in technical planning. Man's progress was such that he was subduing a great river to make the Indian desert productive. Smothered in clouds of dust, workmen crawled ant-like round massive concrete constructions whose foundations were embedded in prehistoric deposits containing the Stone-Age rubbish dumps of flint tools which represented the object of our excursion. Paterson led us off into some limestone hills strewn with waste-flakes, some of which might have served as digging and hoeing implements. Disappointing though it was not to find flint artefacts of this sort in geologically datable strata, their shape and distribution suggested that a primitive form of agriculture had preceded the first permanent settlement of the western borders of India. They were relics of a culture on whose soil there later arose the Indus Valley civilization whose ruins at Mohenjo-Daro we planned to visit in a few days' time.

These neolithic work-sites would have struck us as less significant had they not been situated in the vicinity of one of the main centres of Indus civilization. The ruins of Mohenjo-Daro suggest that they belonged to an urban metropolis which maintained relations with the Mesopotamian empire of Sumer, but neither area yielded any clues to the period when the first permanent settlements were established in the basins of the Indus or Euphrates. This turned our attention to an archaeological problem which was still unsolved at that time, namely, the relationship between the earliest river-valley cultures and those of the adjoining Iranian highlands. Since then, archaeological research in the region of the Iranian plateau has elicited proof that the earliest cultures spread from there into the lowlands about half way through the 4th millennium B.C. The archaeological data which I had latterly been culling from literature on the subject indicated that the extension of agriculture followed certain river networks which favoured hoeing and digging.

Geographical limitations of this sort surely lead one to conclude that the emergence of socialization in the neolithic period was essentially dependent on such factors, and that the development of man's new-found knowledge of fertility was expedited by favourable geographical conditions. The earliest examples of pottery in these regions, which include female clay figures and ceramic ornaments, disclose that a cosmic sense of life, rooted in fertility-magic, endowed the neolithic period with a universal artistic symbolism governed by magic. Sedentary man suddenly acquired a much broader awareness of his relationship to Nature. The magic of Stone-Age hunters and cave dwellers began to add substantially to their realm of experience by embracing the generative and procreative forces of Nature. Not only did plant-cultivation and stock-breeding—in addition to hunting—engender new religious ideas, but men began to organize themselves and so take their first step toward civilization proper.

Stimulated by archaeological observations in the Indus Valley, notions like these paved the way for Teilhard's ideas on the *biological evolution of history*. As a student of the evolution of life, he looked upon cultural history as a 'special form of zoological development', as part of the over-all unfolding of life. To a certain extent, civilizations are a continuation of genus- and species-development on a higher, that is, psychically conceived plane. Their collective units were governed less by organic than by psychical factors, which was why 'forms of liberty emerged in the interplay of life-forces which had hitherto been very rare or even entirely unknown.'[1] In this way,

[1] *Le Groupe zoölogique humain*, p. 116 et seq.

history as a biological process is not only absorbed into the continuum of life-forces but seen as a planetary process which must necessarily embrace all environmental relationships. Surprising and ingenious though this biological approach to history seems, particularly when contrasted with the tidy regularity envisaged by Spengler and Toynbee, it is not as novel as it at first appears. The novelty of Teilhard's historical approach lies more in its phenomenological relationship to his general world of ideas, in its connexion with his concept of universal growth in psychical powers and their culmination in 'consciousness' or self-awareness. Apart from that, his biological or, rather, scientific interpretation of history was, to my knowledge, first developed by the German geographers who elaborated the theories of Friedrich Ratzel, a pupil of Wagner, the Munich ethnologist. Ratzel was the founder of anthropogeography, which relates the races and cultures of mankind to the geographical environment and its fluctuating fortunes. As in Teilhard's case, this conception of the geographically conditioned nature of cultural and historical processes was based on evolutionist ideas. Indeed, one can say that Ratzel's ideas were an aftermath of Darwinism, which held that the struggle for existence, as expressed in adaptation to geographical and other conditions, had a vital bearing on the evolution of the species. The American geographer and explorer Ellsworth Huntington devoted numerous works to the subject of environmental influences on man, particularly the influence of climatic changes on the history of ancient civilizations. However, this geographical slant on history has nothing to do with Teilhard's concept of phylogenesis or, rather, 'psychogenesis', for Teilhard saw the grouping of races and cultures and their mutual interaction as an actual phylogenic process whose study he rightly hoped would yield him new and important insights into the meaning of history.

Just as historical research has until now seen its main task as the collection and limited interpretation of documentary evidence, so it is with present-day archaeology, of which a gifted anthropologist once said that it had sold its birthright for a mess of potsherds. Critical times like these should inspire scholars to contribute to the ideological orientation of our age, just as Teilhard's ideas have stimulated cultural research.

While on the subject of our encounter with the archaeological treasures of the Indus Valley, I think it worth quoting one of Teilhard's letters,[2] in which he relates the concept of progress to his current impressions.

> Last week we went to Sind, towards Baluchistan; there we found astonishing palaeolithic and neolithic workshops in a plateau rising up from the alluvial basin of the Indus—impossible, unfortunately, to work out the stratigraphy properly. It is picturesque country in which the sun, the sands, the fertile alluvium and the forests of date-palms reminded me vividly of Egypt. We went out of our way to look at the famous excavations at Mohenjo-Daro (one of the centres of the Indus civilization). In the middle of the tamarisk bush you find a red-brick town, partially exposed since 1922, with its houses, drains, streets, wells and water system. . . . More than 3000 years before our era, people were living there who

[2] *Letters from a Traveller*, p. 216.

played with dice like our own, fished with hooks like ours, and wrote in characters we can't yet read. We live surrounded by ideas and objects infinitely more ancient than we imagine; and yet at the same time everything is in motion. The universe is a vast thing in which we should be lost if it did not converge upon the Person.

Personification in Teilhard's sense is the growth of consciousness, perceived in geological terms, towards which the mental forces operative in organic evolution tend.[3] It seems to me that this conception can shed new light on the history of ancient civilizations. Its motive power is the gradual relaxation of a primitive mental subjection to the elemental and animal forces of Nature. Both in the extinct civilizations of the past and in those of modern primitive peoples, the primordial immaturity of man expresses itself in demonic experience. Mythical creatures, together with bulls, lions and deer, appear in grotesque combinations on the seals of the Indus Valley culture. Under the spell of their power, these early city-dwellers believed they could see supernatural figures which they sought to conjure up by means of magic rites. Animal demonism, originally rife among Ice-Age hunters and visually depicted in cave paintings, was a mental heritage which the growth of consciousness

[3] 'Human energy presents itself to our view as the term of a vast process in which the whole mass of the Universe is involved. In us, the evolution of the World towards the spirit becomes conscious. From that moment, our perfection, our interest, our salvation demand only that we press on with all our strength. We cannot yet understand exactly where it will lead us, but it would be absurd for us to doubt that it will lead us towards some end of supreme value.' *Cahiers Pierre Teilhard de Chardin I*, 'Building the Earth', Éditions du Seuil, Paris 1958, p. 26.

gradually reabsorbed. Teilhard regarded this 'heightening of consciousness, understanding and scope of operation' as a phase in the process which he described as the 'totalization' of humanity, that is, the concentration and unification of mental energies.[4] Viewed in that light, the ruins of ancient civilizations may to some extent serve as gauges of human dynamism. Just as one can trace the evolutionary trend in a group of animals from fossils, so archaeological sites illustrate the course of human evolution. In this respect, the ruins of Mohenjo-Daro provided an interesting insight into the total difference between the development of mind and technique. While wandering through the excavated city we were considerably impressed by the methodical lay-out of the streets, which evoked automatic comparisons with New York. Both places have the same broad thoroughfares or avenues intersected at right angles by numerous narrower streets. The modern impression created by this arrangement is matched by the sewerage system, which is technically advanced enough to merit comparison with that of medieval European towns. The general lay-out of India's earliest large urban settlement seems to have been adapted to climatic conditions and to have paid some attention to the requirements of hygiene. What about the spiritual requirements of this town, with its relatively advanced level of technical planning?

If any conclusions can be drawn from the seals and works of art displayed in the museum at Mohenjo-Daro, it is that the same sort of animal magic was practised there as in ancient Egypt and Babylon. However, there is a very Indian flavour about the worship of the bull

[4] *Le Groupe zoölogique humain*, p. 129 et seq.

and other creatures such as deer, tiger and rhinoceros—i.e., wild beasts of the type worshipped and portrayed by cave-dwellers. The deity in animal guise—a belief inherited from the Stone Age—coupled with modern-seeming town planning . . . we found it an incongruous combination. This was yet another case where technical progress had outstripped spiritual development, much as, in European history, the art of printing preceded the spiritual revolutions of the 16th and 18th centuries.

To the extent that technology is an expression of human consciousness, a similar discrepancy between material and spiritual development can be identified in our own time, for technology is quite clearly pointing the way to a new phase in human existence. Are not radio and television, jet planes and space exploration laying the foundations of a new world-wide existence, a great era of human co-operation? By extending the individual's radius of action, technology is bound to unite humanity in larger cultural and political groups and lead to a more universal penetration of ideas which revolve increasingly round the common destiny of mankind. This is obviously the intensification of consciousness which has for a century been effecting a greater amalgamation of the economic, technical and social forces that are forging a network of new links around the world; the intensification which, Teilhard believed, leads to cohesion.

Thus, if modern technology is paving the way for planetary consciousness, just as in earlier times man-made irrigation systems or the alloying of metals gave a fillip to socio-political organization, it may be regarded as evidence of that special form of evolution which constitutes the growth of consciousness. Seen in this way, man is not the end-product of an infinite process of organic development, but its new medium. Once technology had conquered distance, it ushered in a new age of knowledge and planning—our own age, with its early essays in establishing world-wide organizations devoted to more intensive economic and cultural exchanges. Being at an experimental stage, we cannot afford to dissipate our energies by yielding to petty doubts, but must, like Teilhard, take a broad view of the present, sustained by a faith founded on careful research.[5] As far as his ideas on the progressive evolution of mankind were based on geological study, they and their logical inferences have a convincing ability to lend the present condition of man a deeper meaning and endow humanity with faith in the future.

But to return to 1935; Paterson had reported the existence of numerous palaeolithic work-sites in Southern India, so we looked forward to finding similar traces of palaeolithic habitation in Central India. The idea of an ancient culture distributed throughout India seemed to attract Teilhard, for he had frequently spoken during our journey of a universal dissemination of fossil man in the Middle Quaternary. From this aspect, Central India presented us with a potential opportunity to fill in a large gap in our knowledge of the earliest human civilizations. Teilhard's ultimate aim was to make a contribution to the problem of dates and of the dissemination of ancient cultures in Asia.

The chosen point of departure for our next trip was a village in the neighbourhood of Hoshangabad, where we stayed in one of the usual government bungalows. The

[5] See also p. 103.

valley and its numerous fields were velvety green with winter rain, and in places, especially beside the river itself, streaked with grey and reddish earth-tones which gave immediate promise of fossil-bearing outcrops. Our very first day's search of the steep river-bank yielded bones and teeth belonging to buffaloes, elephants, hippopotami and crocodiles. Among these fossil bones Teilhard identified species typical of the time of Java and Peking Man, and this at once aroused our hopes of finding traces of early men. Next day we were fortunate enough to discover the first stone tools in the fossil-bearing layers. We had been making our way along the river-bank, searching slowly and painstakingly, when Teilhard suddenly called out something in an excited voice from a spur of rock. When I reached him he held out a piece of dark quartzite, a broad-bladed *coup de poing*, similar to those of the Acheul culture, which he had dug out of a layer in the side of the bank, together with a hippopotamus-tooth. As always on such occasions, Teilhard waited a while before making any definite pronouncement on his find, especially as it not only represented the first tool of its kind to be found in Central India but was discovered beside the remains of an animal which early man had undoubtedly hunted. While recalling similar examples in Europe, it occurred to him that this type of implement had very probably been used for killing or dissecting hippopotami, since its broad blade would have been particularly suited to the purpose. Experience told us that we could expect to find other palaeolithic artefacts in the same layer, so the succeeding days were devoted to an intensive search for them. As it turned out, not only did we find a substantial number of different tools, but the smaller tools which came to light in more recent layers indicated the presence of a younger culture as well. Since we now had proof of a palaeolithic culture in the Narbada Valley which differed from that of North-West India, we began to ponder on possible connexions with other sites of discovery in Southern India and on the question of whether Java and Peking Man could have manufactured such tools. No evidence was yet forthcoming from Java, and the caches of artefacts found near Peking were very much more primitive than the Narbada tools, so I was compelled to agree with Teilhard's conjecture that the hypothetical primitive man of India might have been of a different type and date. It followed from the finds made in Java that man had appeared in several forms early in the course of evolution, and it was these finds which Teilhard proposed to examine in the near future. I was struck by the eager anticipation with which he looked forward to his trip to Java, almost as if he guessed that Dr von Koenigswald's discoveries there would supply entirely new evidence for his theory of the origin of man.

I recall one particular evening when we returned to the rest-house at dusk. Countless little oil-lamps of the sort used by the Hindus when celebrating their religious festivals twinkled like fire-flies between the village huts. With its groups of palms and venerable mango-trees, the whole place seemed to have been transformed into a setting for some oriental *Midsummer Night's Dream*. The caretaker of our bungalow told us that the villagers were holding an extempore festival in honour of Siva. Apparently, the god had visited their fields a few days ago in the guise of a flood, leaving behind numerous symbols of his procreative power in the shape of some longish pebbles, which were regarded as an especial mark of divine favour. From the temple, where festivities were in full swing, came the sound of flutes and drums and the nasal incantations of the priest. The caretaker advised us to go down to the river, where the villagers would soon be releasing their 'light-ships'. When we reached the bank we saw a group of women standing on the stone steps customarily used for washing or bathing. They were busying themselves with small pieces of wood, on which they laid burning wicks. Laughing and chattering, they filed down the steps and committed their small illuminated craft to the current. The ghostly little lights soon vanished except for a few, which reached the bend in the river. This seemed to be the moment for which several of the women had been waiting, for they clapped their hands and broke into cries of delight. If they managed to follow their light to the river-bend, the caretaker informed us, it was an omen of fertility. The whole village seemed to be involved in the festival. In several houses we glimpsed old men seated at table by candle-light, holding their hands before their foreheads in prayer, Hindu-fashion, and chanting continuously from books with such devotion that for a moment we felt ourselves carried back in time to the far-off days when the Vedic hymns still formed part of daily worship.

> The real peninsular India: mild summer weather (21 December); golden light; a countryside thickly shaded with mangoes and banyans, fine bushy trees like ancient oaks; tall ridges covered with thick forests (tiger jungle); peacocks in the jungle; crocodiles in the river; parrots in the gardens; at

every corner frolicking bands of big black-faced monkeys with white ruffs; very gentle, even gracious, people living in big, beautifully clean huts; the women red-veiled, the men in white.[6]

Then there were the fakirs squatting beneath the broad branches of mango-trees, their naked torsos smeared with ash and their long matted hair piled turban-like atop their ascetic faces—hideous caricatures of human beings whom Teilhard regarded with compassion, likening them to 'spirits of the underworld'. Just as the fakirs reminded him of the human bondage caused by religious fanaticism, so he was disgusted by the caste-mark tradition. If there were any foreigner in the area who could have roused ancient India to new life, it was Teilhard. In this superstition-ridden Indian world, he seemed like a new species of human being.

During our last days in the district we got a guide to take us to see the rock-paintings near Hoshangabad, which Indian literature on the subject described as being of comparatively recent date. They depicted battles between two entirely alien groups of warriors. A troop of pale-skinned, mounted men armed with swords and shields is falling upon a band of dark-skinned archers—immediately identifiable as a primitive tribe, possibly forest-dwellers—who seem, with their bows and arrows, hopelessly inferior to the attackers. As soon as Teilhard had absorbed the scene and the artist's technique, he commented with evident excitement that it was very probably a battle-scene from the time of the Indo-European drive against the aboriginal population of Central India. In his view, therefore, the paintings must

[6] *Letters from a Traveller*, p. 217.

be much older than had hitherto been supposed, and probably dated from the 2nd millennium B.C., which must be regarded as the period when the Indus Valley civilization met its downfall at the hands of foreign invaders. The fifteen hundred miles which separated us from Mohenjo-Daro suddenly became a bridge linking us with one of the major events in India's history and one which had radically altered the country's spiritual and social structure.

It was remarkable how quickly Teilhard invested such impressions with significance. In his company, one could always bank on a mental reflex which placed facts in a wider context and seemed to correlate them with Platonic 'ideas'. It was as if whatever he saw was no more than a confirmation of his inward wealth of ideas. When scrutinizing fossils or artefacts, he gave the impression that he had somehow been involved in their formation, that he could grasp their underlying significance by means of a kind of inner eye. This unusual gift may account for his dislike of expert classification, a necessary task but one which he gladly left to others. It was a characteristic which he shared with other scientists, e.g. Alexander von Humboldt, who much preferred his assistants to write up the details of botanical or mineralogical research. However, the salient experience to be gained from working with Teilhard was of his ability to invest the most inanimate material with life and ply one with a constant stream of ideas, thereby assuring one of the existence of a spiritual domain in which it somehow became urgently necessary to believe.

At the same time, Teilhard was the last person to behave in an arrogant or sermonizing way. He always adapted himself to his milieu, never condescended and never waxed didactic when speaking as an authority, just as he never demanded special treatment on a trip, even under conditions of extreme discomfort, but 'fitted in' with a humility which put us all to shame. But what left an indelible impression on me during our last days in Central India was one particular incident. One day, having heard of some more rock-drawings, we resolved to inspect them without delay. According to our informant, they were situated near a road leading southwards through the mountain forests, so we were compelled to leave our car after a short distance and take to a narrow footpath. As we were picking our way through dense undergrowth in the shade of some huge trees, it suddenly occurred to me that we were in a noted game preserve and might well meet a panther at any moment. The idea of falling unarmed into the clutches of such a beast filled me with apprehension for Teilhard as well as myself. Oppressed by such thoughts, I strode ahead of him, so firmly convinced that every rustle in the dark undergrowth denoted the presence of a lurking predator that it was on the tip of my tongue to suggest retracing our steps. When I turned back to communicate my fears, I saw my companion standing motionless, his eyes fixed on a thicket from which came a loud sound of snapping twigs. Involuntarily, I seized his arm. 'This forest is like a sea of hidden life,' he said, regarding me with veiled eyes. I should have known that, while I was giving way to fear, Teilhard simply felt like one creature among many.

Looking back on this incident, I find that it exactly matches the impressions which I gained of Teilhard's fearlessness on other occasions. At such moments, he was sustained by the inner sense of assurance which had distinguished him on the battlefields in the First World War, when he collected wounded men and took them to the nearest dressing-station under a hail of fire. When his friend Max Bégouën asked him how he managed to remain so calm, he replied: 'If I'm killed I'll just change my state, that's all.' This belief may have helped him to endure the many dangers to which he exposed himself during a lifetime of scientific exploration.

Although I cannot remember the exact circumstances of our leave-taking, I know that we parted in Delhi as friends, certain that we should some day resume the studies which had begun so auspiciously in India. Whether this would be in Upper India or in some other part of South Asia, only the future could tell.

IV

Teilhard's full life suggests that he must have worn seven-league boots and been as familiar with railway time-tables and sailing lists as a member of the big-business fraternity. His constant journeyings between and across continents had a natural bearing on his role as an independent researcher in the world of science. He was as much in demand as an authority on special fields of prehistory as on those of palaeontology and geology, nor should one forget the personal charm which captivated so many of his colleagues. To repeat, the world was his laboratory, and he felt so at home in it, whatever the circumstances, that despite his restless mode of existence he could be described as a constant in a world of variables. Once, when I complained to him about the strains and stresses of my own professional life, he remarked that a chequered career is often the most fruitful.

In view of this trait in his character, it was hardly surprising that, a year after his trip to India and Java, he readily accepted an invitation to visit the United States to attend a conference on prehistory which I was arranging in Philadelphia. In the autumn of 1936, I and Dr Edgar B. Howard, the American prehistorian working at the Museum of Natural History there, had worked out plans for a meeting of leading scientists, its aim being to provide an opportunity for mutual discussions on major questions affecting the origin and evolution of man in the Old and New Worlds. The Carnegie Foundation of New York was to defray the expenses of invited guests, among them several of Teilhard's friends who, like Dr von Koenigswald, had found important human fossils. A number of the latter were to be exhibited at Philadelphia, a prospect which would afford Teilhard opportunities for discussion. Hot on the heels of our invitation came a communication from Peking requesting another invitation for Dr von Koenigswald, who had meanwhile already announced his attendance.

Teilhard arrived in mid-March 1937 and became a welcome guest at the suburban house outside Philadelphia where my wife and I had been living since summer 1936. Although we were the only people he knew in that historic city, he immediately felt at home there and looked forward to an early reunion with other friends made on previous visits to the United States. He was mainly known among experts there for his share in the explorations conducted in the Gobi Desert by Dr R. C. Andrews in 1930. However, his research in China had brought him into contact with the eminent palaeontologist Professor Henry F. Osborn and other members of the American Museum of Natural History as early as 1923, and his publications on fossil finds and prehistoric cultures had contributed in no small degree to the major successes achieved by the large-scale American project. I myself had followed the progress of these expeditions into the Asian interior with the greatest interest because in 1927-8 I had taken part, as a geologist, in the expedition led by the Munich geographer Dr Emil Trinkler, which travelled from Kashmir via Tibet to Chinese Turkestan. In spring 1929 I met Professor Osborn in New York, and it was he who first told me about Teilhard. Like all who knew him, Osborn spoke of him with sincere admiration. Shortly afterwards I also had the opportunity of meeting Professor George E. Barbour, a friend and associate of Teilhard who had not only participated as a geologist in research on Peking Man but had undertaken numerous trips with Teilhard in China. Barbour had accompanied him to the International Geological Congress at Washington in summer 1933 and had, in response to an invitation from myself, delivered an address to Yale University in New Haven. This so stimulated me that I resolved to continue the work which I had begun in Northern India in 1932.

The lecture which Teilhard delivered on 19 March dealt with the Quaternary period in China.[1] It aroused

[1] This report appeared as an article in the book *Early Man*, edited by George G. MacCurdy, Philadelphia 1937, pp. 211-20.

particular interest in that it brought news of fire-utilization and tool-making by Peking Man, whose age is estimated at several hundred thousand years. The way in which Teilhard compared China's earliest palaeolithic cultures with those of Europe, rejecting the idea of any affinity between them, prompted me to refer, during the ensuing debate, to possible relationships between the primitive cultures of Asia and America, which seemed to have an important bearing on the origin of man in the New World. Once again, Teilhard's way of looking at prehistory in a wider context had exercised a stimulating effect, because no specialized work can be properly evaluated except in relation to broader questions. He had a natural faculty for endowing detailed work with greater meaning, for projecting the classification of prehistoric tools, for instance, on to a plane where they could contribute to the general picture of early human evolution and thus acquire philosophical significance. In view of the philosophical objectives underlying his scientific labours, one could only marvel at the extreme care with which he confined his remarks during such lectures to factual observations, never giving his expert audiences occasion to become aware of their aversion to, or even abhorrence of, philosophical expositions.

The organizers of the conference had planned to bestow academic honours on various guests, among them Teilhard, who was to receive the Gregor Mendel Medal from the Catholic College at Villanova, a suburb of Philadelphia. This prize was awarded for outstanding contributions to biological research by scientists of the Catholic persuasion, and since previous recipients of the medal included a number of eminent scholars there was every reason for Teilhard to accept such an honour. Accompanying him to the banquet given in his honour by the President of the College on 22 March, I became aware of the special significance of the occasion. It was probably his first opportunity to expound his ideas on the origin of man before an audience composed of American university men and ecclesiastics. Teilhard spoke of the importance of prehistoric research to our knowledge of man and of the need to see human destiny in geological terms. He had made a few notes on a small piece of paper which he held in his hand during his brief speech after the presentation of the medal, but he never referred to them. His mode of speaking, with which I became familiar on subsequent occasions, made absolutely no concession to the time-honoured tradition, particularly common in the United States, whereby audiences are treated to a light and humorous introduction. He spoke in the literary style characteristic of him, with a certain inwardness and mental agility which sometimes made it hard to grasp the true meaning of a turn of phrase immediately. I got the impression that his address to the assembled guests failed to evoke any real echo, probably because very few of them had sufficient special knowledge to be able to follow his reasoning. Apart from this, however, his remarks were hardly calculated to create a favourable impression in this particular milieu, since they referred, if only by implication, to human evolution, a subject which the curriculum of any Catholic college in America treated with extreme caution at this period. In view of this, I had to admire the candour with which Teilhard approached his theme. It was as though he were determined to proclaim his ideas on the origin and destiny of man not only, as heretofore, to a limited circle of friends, but to the world at large. My supposition was to be confirmed in the days that followed.

Shortly after the opening of the conference, our house-guest gave an interview to a reporter from the *New York Times*. The report, which occupied an entire column in that influential paper next day, gave a sensationalized account of Teilhard's novel ideas on the origin of man. It read as though he supported the Darwinian theory, a patently inaccurate interpretation which totally disregarded his basic concept of the predestination of organic evolution, a process which had found its supreme expression in man.[2] I remember Teilhard complaining about the way the interview had been misrepresented and saying that he was anxious for a chance to rectify the situation. Such an opportunity arose shortly after the presentation of the Gregor Mendel Medal. A reporter from a leading Canadian newspaper arrived at the house and spent a long time closeted with our guest. From personal experience, I felt it my duty to warn Teilhard against the further misunderstandings which might arise from such publicity, but he firmly insisted on seizing the opportunity. Satisfied though he was with the result, the new report seemed to me to do little to expunge the sensational impression created by its predecessor, and I was filled with foreboding on his behalf.

As it turned out, an incident occurred after Teilhard's

[2] Although the *New York Times* report of 19 March 1937 stressed Teilhard's view that the concept of human evolution in no way militated against his religion, the impression created by the headline was that Peking Man represented a 'missing link' in the Darwinian or Haeckelian sense.

departure on which I can only report at second hand. He was to have received an honorary degree from the Catholic University of Boston, but found on arrival that the honour could not be granted. Had the authorities taken exception to the newspaper reports? Whatever the truth, Teilhard's attempt to make his ideas known to a wider circle in America encountered considerable resistance. I surmise that, in a country so noted for its liberal-mindedness, he had banked on being able to speak out with greater freedom. In fact, he could readily have found a receptive audience in certain academic or literary circles, but he made no attempt to contact them at this juncture.

I find it deplorable that Teilhard's great wealth of ideas had to remain hidden for so long, especially when one considers the hundreds of thousands of readers in so many countries who have been enriched by his posthumous publications. One also wonders how it was possible that his private anxiety at the course of world events never encouraged him to adopt a public stand. Continental Europe was being swept by a wind of crisis and Communist and Fascist ideas were in direct conflict, having created two sets of ideological values whose very opposition ran counter to what Teilhard wanted: an awareness of man's common destiny. There is no doubt that he found the sight of this dissension literally oppressive, yet he must have been quite as aware of the impact created by the two hostile camps as of their underlying motives, which betrayed a yearning for new forms of social order. During these years he resembled someone who looks down on an arena in which the contestants are battling with insensate fury over values which he recognizes as false. Events in Philadelphia and Boston ought also to be viewed in this light. Certainly, their importance in his life should not be underestimated, since they convey a hint of the conflict between his mind and the forces which wanted to limit its scope of operations.

Amid all this excitement, we found time to discuss future plans. We considered the possibility of pursuing our joint research in Southern Asia, a scheme which appealed to Teilhard if only because political upheavals in China boded ill for the future and were threatening his continued work there. Since attention had been focused on the island of Java by recent discoveries of fossil human remains, and since Dr John C. Merriam, President of the Carnegie Institution and a palaeontologist, was taking a benevolent interest in further studies there, we contemplated the possibility of supplementing the results gained in India by undertaking research in neighbouring areas of South-East Asia. Dr von Koenigswald, too, seemed prepared to introduce us to his fruitful area of exploration. Accordingly, I started on preliminary arrangements for this new project shortly after Teilhard's departure, and was emboldened in June 1937 to invite him to take part. He had left America for Paris by then, and on 3 July he wrote me a letter from his family château. What follows is the original English text, with a few personal and technical remarks omitted:

My Dear Helmut,

I have received with a great joy, this morning, your letter of June 19. The news you gave me are very good, and, since I feel all right now, the project of the Burma trip sounds very exciting. The 15th of

November is perhaps a bit early for me; but I think we can adjust the dates rather easily: I think I might, at the worst, arrive two weeks later, and join you somewhere North of Rangoon.

In the meantime, I plan to leave Paris via Siberia at the middle of August. The sooner I can see the specimens collected in S. China (Yunnan) during the last spring, and discuss with Bien (who has spent several months there), the better it will be. By giving me a precise plan of work for the immediate future, your letter has been for me a positive relief, and I begin already to forget that I had to give up the Siberian excursion.—Pei (the Chinese prehistorian) leaves Paris just now, after getting successfully his degrees, so that I will have him back in Peking with me, in September. . . .

Nothing new, besides. Since almost a fortnight, I am enjoying a good rest in the country, in Auvergne: an old family house, along the Allier river, perfectly quiet. Everything is so richly green. Here are living one of my brothers, his wife . . . , I go back to Paris in three days.

By the way, I found my moral standard much higher than I suspected, even amongst my colleagues, in France. Evidently, the magnitude of the present social events has opened the best eyes on the nature of the changes which we are undergoing now; and the conception of 'Human Energy as a whole' will be very soon a banal thing. My various typewritten papers are spreading fast, and nobody objects.—The editors of the rather conservative *Review* (where I am staying in Paris) have asked me an article on

> Sinanthropus (essentially the same things which have so much disturbed my American colleagues) which is to be published in the next number; and possibly the article on the '*Front Humain*' will be accepted too.—I am much more interested in a new Essay which is maturing now in my mind (on Human Energy, precisely).[3]

This letter seems to me to illustrate the twin poles which dominated Teilhard's life at that period: devotion to research, and the struggle to disseminate and gain recognition for his ideas. He yearned to pursue the problem of man's ancestry in fields which gave promise of solving certain questions, for instance, the extent and relative age of early traces of man in Southern Asia. India and Java had furnished him with new information, and in Southern China his Chinese assistant, Bien, had come across caves containing fossils which might well shed new light on the precursors of Peking Man. There was a chance that we should make new finds in Burmese-Chinese border regions which are readily accessible from the Irrawaddy Valley. I had already told Teilhard in Philadelphia about some Stone-Age tools found in Burma by a British geologist shortly before.

The scientist carries ideas about much as a woman carries unborn children, dependent on them without having any real preconception of them. As long as there was a chance of finding fresh clues to the origin of man in South-East Asia, Teilhard was determined to exploit it in my company. It was also one way of temporarily

[3] Extracts from these essays were published posthumously in *Cahiers Teilhard de Chardin*, Éditions du Seuil, Paris 1958.

avoiding the uncertainties which Japanese infiltration into China had created for him and his colleagues.

Although the foregoing letter is dominated by professional considerations like these, the passage referring to the recognition of Teilhard's ideas in France seems to me to be particularly significant in the general context of his life. To him, anthropogenesis was a supreme manifestation of psychical energies which had taken millions of years to evolve from the animal, indeed, the microcosmic orders of life. It was 'creative evolution' in the Bergsonian sense, but conceived of in more direct relationship to man. With the birth of consciousness, psychical energy had taken a leap forward which must be interpreted not as an accidental mutation but as a necessary consequence and coercive development of mental substance, manifest, from the purely physical aspect, in the development of brain and skull. The whole evolution of organic life has been dominated by the central impulse toward consciousness, and it is to this that man owes his origin.

In the normal way, it would have been simple enough for a philosopher and writer with an academic background to find a home for such ideas, particularly in France, where Bergson had carved out a central niche for the evolutionary phenomenon in modern philosophical thought. In Teilhard's case, however, circumstances were far less auspicious. Although the religious order to which he belonged is noted for its comparative tolerance of novel views, Teilhard seemed to have to fight for recognition. Much as he was respected within his order as a scientist of international standing, a fact which brought him many advantages during his lifetime, his independence necessarily engendered obstacles which had to be surmounted. But then, which of the spiritual pioneers, whether ecclesiastic or layman, has not encountered deafness and blindness in the outside world, and which of them has not had to beg or fight for a hearing? It is always their lot to carve a path through the tangled undergrowth of traditional thought, a path which begins with the action of their personality on others which may come into contact with it, a path through gloom to enlightenment. In Teilhard's case, his studies and voyages of scientific exploration, together with the official posts which he held from time to time in Paris and Peking, brought him a series of personal contacts, some of which quickly blossomed into worth-while friendships. He could count on a sympathetic hearing from his intimate circle, therefore, but as he grew older this ceased to be enough for him. His ideas needed wider dissemination, hence the satisfaction with which he wrote to me of the publications that were being planned in Paris. Only someone familiar with the scientific, religious and political conditions prevailing in France at that time could describe the complex position in which Teilhard found himself. The special circumstances of our crisis-ridden age are an intimation of how many obstacles and impediments combined to prevent his breaking free. Only death could release him, but by then the opportunity to spread his views on the destiny of man and his special kind of faith by word of mouth was irretrievably lost.

As he wrote to his friend Max Bégouën from Peking, in a letter dated 21 October 1937:[4]

[4] *Letters from a Traveller*, pp. 232-3.

> For me personally, the most serious aspect is that all my colleagues, Chinese and foreign, are unanimous in agreeing that my place, *for the time being*, is here and not in Burma, where de Terra expects me at the beginning of December. And it would have been so important for me to go to Burma! I shall wait a little while longer before I finally decide; but I am very much afraid that it will soon be impossible to be in two minds about where my duty lies: I must stay here.

One can understand how reluctant he was to desert his regular place of work at a time of such great political unrest in China, especially as there was a plan afoot to evacuate the Chinese scientific authorities (the Geological Survey of China), for whom he worked as a palaeontologist, to Nanking. In addition, he had suffered an attack of malaria shortly before returning to Peking, and his colleagues advised him against visiting the tropics. However, when a Chinese colleague, Dr Pei, suddenly offered to stand in for him, he sailed for Burma from Tientsin in December 1937.

V

I was not at all worried by doubts as to whether Teilhard would participate in my expedition. Knowing how keen he was to continue his Indian studies in South-East Asia, I had gone ahead with my preparations, which involved enlisting the support of several institutes and the services of Dr Hallam L. Movius of Harvard University and his wife. In view of all my self-imposed responsibilities, a sudden refusal on Teilhard's part would undoubtedly have been a painful blow, especially as we were counting on his help in examining the Javanese sites which had shed so much new light on the problem of man's ancestry.

No one who enjoyed Teilhard's friendship and scientific collaboration could escape the lasting influence which radiated from his personality. One felt a sort of obligation toward him which seemed to transcend any obstacle which may have arisen from external factors of a professional or political nature. The mental intensity with which he approached scientific problems communicated itself with magnetic effect, so that, infected by his vigour, one felt tempted to regard any joint project as already completed—even before the first steps toward its realization had been taken. Only this can explain why I disregarded his written allusions to all kinds of obstacles and was still unperturbed by lack of news when I and my wife met the Movius'es in Calcutta on 14 November 1937. From there we took a boat to Rangoon, whence we travelled up the Irrawaddy by river-steamer to Yenangyaung, where I and Dr Movius made a start on some field-work.

We had counted on Teilhard's arriving in Burma during December, but had to possess our souls in patience until the very last day of the month. Reaching Rangoon, via Hongkong and Singapore, on 28 December, he found my detailed instructions for the remainder of the journey awaiting him. I can see him now, waving to us from the deck of the antiquated paddle-steamer as it berthed at the landing-stage of a small township north of Mandalay. As in India, his kit was of the simplest and consisted of two modest suitcases which he could easily have managed by himself if our driver had not carried them straight from the boat to the car. His tanned features betrayed no hint of the trials and tribulations which had attended his journey from Peking. Passages from letters dated 16 and 17 December describe them in the following terms:

> I left Tientsin in a small cargo ship bound for Hongkong (no easy matter just now, embarking at Tientsin—ice and mud) and yesterday I had the luck to find another at Swatow, carrying Chinese emigrants to Malaya. This will take me in four days to Singapore, and there I have a good chance of getting a steamer fairly soon for Rangoon, where I am sure to find instructions from de Terra. So that's that. I find it most odd to be transported suddenly into the tropics, when ten days ago I was resigning myself to a winter in Peking.[1]

On the following day, he wrote to his brother:

> . . . in a small steamer carrying Chinese immigrants, I am back again after three months on the blue expanse of the Malayan seas, not a little surprised at no longer freezing in the icy weather of Peking.
>
> I came on board with some difficulty at ice-bound Tangku, and had the good luck to find in Swatow, before we reached Hongkong, a small cargo vessel bound for Singapore. If I have any luck at Singapore, I can be in Rangoon before 13th January. I hardly hoped it would go so well. If everything works out as it should, I expect to return to Peking

[1] *Letters from a Traveller*, pp. 234-5.

> about the beginning of March, after spending the winter in the warm and with the satisfaction of my duty accomplished.[2]

We were glad to have been able to meet him at the little landing-stage north of Mandalay, and could only hope that his arduous journey from Peking would repay itself in the coming months. It was fortunate that during our drive to the Shan plateau the same day we were able to introduce him to the tropical forest, which transforms the rainy eastern margin of the highlands into an animal paradise. The road winds its way upwards from the Irrawaddy Valley through thick forests in which small species of deer such as the muntjak, together with rhinoceros, tiger, buffalo and crocodile, recall the diverse animal community which existed in the Himalayas during the Tertiary period. We must have halted briefly somewhere in the forest, for I remember that at one stage we tried to locate some gibbons—long-armed anthropoid apes—whose cries issued from the branches of the forest giants surrounding us. We never met them face to face, but their proximity was like a primeval echo from the period, millions of years in duration, when the higher primates were transforming themselves into manlike creatures. Enclosed by such wilderness, I could always sense, in Teilhard's company, something of the mystical empathy with Nature which made him listen keenly for animal calls and sometimes provoked him to merriment. Anyone who reads his letters will find him to be an artist who could reproduce impressions of Nature in graphic prose.

Leafing through his *Letters from a Traveller*, one repeatedly

[2] *Letters from a Traveller*, p. 235.

comes across passages which convey his sensitive powers of observation.

> We arrived at Penang late in the afternoon, under a stormy sky, copper and inky black. It's the first time I've had an opportunity to take a good look at this scenic paradise . . . our car rolled smoothly over the fine red roads, among forests of coconut palms, with huts built on piles and great umbrella-like trees with a finer profusion of purple flowers than you'd find even in a flower-bed. Night came all too soon for us.

Of the ancient temple-city of Pagan, which we visited in January, he wrote:

> From where I am on the verandah I overlook the Irrawaddy, fringed by low mountains and held in a ribbon of green, exactly like the Nile in Upper Egypt. Pagan, the former capital of Burma, is now only a picturesque bazaar, lost among palms and mimosa, but the surroundings are simply one great forest of pagodas, some of them dilapidated red brick, some a vivid white or even gilded, like the dome of the Invalides. The population is very much of a mixture. First the Burmese, all grace and beaming smiles, hair worn in a bun by both men and women, and dressed in dazzling colours, with an extraordinary proportion of orange-robed monks. Towards the Arakan-Yoma you meet the 'Chins', small men with moustaches, almost Mongol. To the east the black-turbanned Shans and a chequerboard of small groups of strange ethnic types. But all these people occupy only an insignificant part of the country itself. Outside the delta the jungle is

> master—very beautiful towards Mogok, with its forests of bamboo and huge teak-trees that are rafted down the Irrawaddy. Marvellous weather. The midday sun is trying, but the nights are cool and the sky permanently cloudless. Such are the advantages of the dry season, which lasts until April. No wonder I feel so well: it's as though I had found a new youth. I can walk indefinitely without getting tired, just as I did in India.[3]

It was not surprising that he felt well. The district of Mogok, where we spent the beginning of 1938, could hardly have failed to create a favourable impression. The bungalow in which we were staying stood in an idyllic garden where poinsettia blossoms, roses and hibiscus flowers glowed amid the green of huge bamboo clumps in which colibris and parakeets fluttered to and fro. Above the broad canopies of mimosa bushes and plane-trees, the pale blue sky swarmed with brown birds of prey, the garadu of Indian mythology, soaring tirelessly and uttering sinister screams. As if endeavouring to surpass its own bright diversity, Nature had filled the ochre soil with treasures—rubies, garnets, greenish tourmalins and other semi-precious stones which find their way, according to shade and size, into the hands of splendour-loving Asiatics or European jewellers. When we insisted on seeing the local mines, Teilhard and I were quite obviously taken for agents of the latter. We asked to be shown how the rich sand was washed and sieved, shook the sieves in muddy water for a few moments and picked out the little grains of precious red and green stone, almost as though we were really on the track of

[3] *Letters from a Traveller*, pp. 236-7.

such things, and not of the fossil bones which formed the real reason for our visit to the mines. Considering the vast extent of the diggings, we had banked on meeting at least one miner who could give us information about fossils, but had to be content with rumours of a Chinese who had found some old bones in a cave. Our interest in such insignificant objects encouraged local jewel-dealers in the erroneous belief that we would pay more for fossils than for rubies. Consequently, some days passed before we were able to question the said Chinese about his finds.

Since the local Chinese enjoyed a reputation for medical skill in this Burmese frontier area, Teilhard cherished hopes of finding some fossil teeth in Chinese apothecaries' shops, where they were sold, together with snakeskin and dried bats' wings, as sovereign remedies. Visiting similar shops in Hongkong and Shanghai, the resourceful Dr von Koenigswald had acquired various teeth belonging to extinct anthropoid apes. These illustrated the remarkable diversity of that group, a factor of great importance to the problem of man's ancestry. The only question was, where had they come from and how could they be classified in chronological order? Chinese apothecaries' statements regarding the origin of such fossils pointed to the interior of Southern China, so it seemed reasonable to connect them with the sites which had recently come to light in that part of China during the exploration of caves. Moreover, this hypothesis fitted in well with the superstitious belief that the fossils were 'dragons' teeth'. Just as there are 'dragons' caves' in European folklore, so there are in that of China, the difference being that the Chinese turn superstition into a lucrative business by offering fossil teeth for sale as miracle cures for every known ailment. Teilhard made fun of this superstition, but I at once noticed how fascinated he was by the prospect of cave exploration, especially in view of the remains of Quaternary vertebrates discovered by one of his Chinese assistants in Yunnan Province a short while before. Caves usually occur in limestone formations, and these contain crevices which often turn out to be veritable mines of fossil remains belonging to land animals, among which, as in the case of Peking Man's discovery-site, relics of early man sometimes come to light. Our geological map of the Mogok region indicated areas of limestone in which we might reasonably expect to find caves and ancient rubble-filled fissures. If money and kind words could prevail on the Chinese to guide us to a fossil site, we should not be the first explorers to have benefited from superstition or popular tradition. Palaeontological research, too, has acquired new information about early man's environment, his art and religious ideas, from excavations made in 'dragons' caves'. The Viennese palaeontologist Othenio Abel, for instance, succeeded in identifying the cave-bear cult of Stone-Age man, a primitive religion still practised until recently by the Samoyeds of Asiatic Russia.

As a palaeontologist and student of prehistory, Teilhard was peculiarly incapable of deriving any interest from this subject, even though he seemed particularly well-qualified to pronounce upon the numinous experiences and symbolism of early man. In view of his original scientific approach and outstanding capacity for interpreting the purpose and evolution of life, one might have expected him to try to evaluate human prehistory from the religious angle. The fact that he refrained from doing so is attributable, perhaps, to the special position which he occupied as a member of the Jesuit Order and a scientist, and which might easily have aroused suspicions, both among his professional colleagues and his fellow-Jesuits, that he was pursuing a highly unorthodox study of religion under the guise of scientific research. Hence his predilection for concrete facts, for the critical identification of fossils and artefacts, for the correct appreciation of geological relationships and for lucid scientific expositions designed to buttress his professional standing. I do not see how he could have behaved otherwise, in his position, without risking the esteem in which he was held by professional circles. Although his main concern was to ascertain how psychical forces combined to give birth to consciousness, and to present a grand synthesis of two apparently incompatible things, religion and science, he managed during his lifetime to conform to the traditional usages of science.

Highly characteristic of the way in which he threaded his way through a mass of scientific detail and put his finger on the crucial issues was his request that our next objective should be to look for palaeolithic tools in the Irrawaddy Valley. This was, as it happened, a valuable suggestion, in that Dr Movius and I had spent the preceding weeks collecting fossils and artefacts there, and had formed certain conclusions about the age of the geological formations in which they were found. We accordingly decided to postpone our cave explorations until the end of February and carry out some geological field-work in an accessible area south of Mandalay. Once again, Teilhard's wealth of experience proved invaluable, for only a few days later he identified as palaeolithic some artefacts which we had been uncertain about until then. He thought they bore an affinity to tools which he had seen on his earlier trip to Java, and since our Burmese finds came from the Middle Quaternary—i.e., corresponded to the age of Java Man—Teilhard found this a good omen for our forthcoming research in Java.

After the evening meal we used to sit outside our tents, where we could survey the broad expanse of the Irrawaddy. Bathed in moonlight, the red of the soil grew pale and the little valleys turned into yawning crevasses. From the village huts, plumes of smoke rose into the silvery night, whose silence was occasionally broken by the bark of a dog. One night, a pack of mangy village mongrels ran round Teilhard's tent, yapping hideously. I heard him reproving them in French, which rather surprised me, since I had often marvelled at how soundly he slept. He could stretch out in the shade of a bush at high noon and fall asleep immediately.

Burmese village dogs remind me of an anecdote told me by someone who accompanied Teilhard on a trip to California. While travelling through New Mexico, they stopped for the night at the house of a noted palaeontologist, high up in the mountains. The evening was spent in animated and protracted discussion, and when Teilhard retired to the guest-room at a late hour he noticed that his breviary had disappeared. Not wishing to disturb his host at midnight, he did not raise the subject until the following morning. After a lengthy search of the house, Teilhard's host handed him back the book, now in a much-dilapidated condition, apologizing for the fact that his dog had used it as a toy and tested his sharp teeth on it as though it were a bone. What lent the animal's misdemeanour special point was the anti-clerical attitude of its master, which had transferred itself, in even more militant form, to his dog!

On one of our evenings in the Irrawaddy Valley, something unforgettable happened which illustrated Teilhard's generosity and friendship. Having made a long excursion up the valley in order to trace the development of certain geological formations, we returned to our camp at nightfall. I had blistered a foot during the lengthy tour, and had just removed my boots with a sigh of relief when I suddenly noticed that my notebook was missing. After a vain search, I was forced to conclude that I had left it at the site we had last examined. We had spent some time there discussing our finds, and would have lingered longer if I had not insisted on our starting back quickly because of approaching darkness. When I told Teilhard that I was going back to fetch my note-book with our Burmese guide he looked quite shocked and said he would go and look for it himself, since it was out of the question for me to walk about in the darkness with my sore foot. Deaf to my entreaties, he pulled on his tennis-shoes, called for the guide and vanished with him into the pitch-black night by the light of a pocket-lamp. When he returned some hours later and brought the notebook to my tent, his whole face was beaming with delight. In fact, he could hardly have done me a greater service, since the book contained a record of all the finds which we had made and discussed together in preceding weeks.

Nothing pleased Teilhard more than to perform some

service which furthered a friend's research. He was devoid of the petty jealousies which so often insinuate themselves into professional circles. By banishing all such trivial considerations, his daily companionship relieved me, as leader of the expedition, of all kinds of worries. He never insisted on being accorded the privileges to which his status as the guest and senior member of our party really entitled him. He always seemed to approve, too, of my daily arrangements in regard to food and accommodation—though their success was due largely to my wife's care and attention.

We had decided, in December, to split up our research programme so that the Moviuses would tour the southern part of the Shan States while the rest of us concentrated on the area round the later celebrated 'Burma Road', which leads to the Chinese border. Before setting off on this tour, we determined to search for artefacts and fossils in some old river-beds near Pagan on the eastern banks of the Irrawaddy.

From there, Teilhard wrote to his brother Joseph on 13 February 1938:

> Our work progresses well in an extraordinarily picturesque setting. At the moment we are camped near an oil-centre: a forest of 'derricks' on ashy hills fortunately doesn't succeed in spoiling the charm of the Irrawaddy. A few days ago we were at Pagan, the ancient capital (before Mandalay) of the Burmese kings. Now it is simply a village lost in palms, banyans, mangoes and mimosa, but surrounded by over a hundred pagodas, some of them in ruins that may well date back to the twelfth century. Nothing really artistic or grand (all brick-built) but

about the whole, particularly when the sun is setting, there is something most fantastic and unreal. I am becoming very fond of this radiant country, three-quarters covered with bush or jungle, in which the most insignificant inhabitant is as graceful and colourful as a flower.

For the last month and more we have been taking advantage of the dryness and the cool weather to work in the low-lying country of Upper Burma. Results—geological and archaeological—have been satisfactory. We have succeeded in sorting out the Irrawaddy formations, where we are collecting abundant evidence of 'old palaeolithic' industry that is completely new. . . This spell in the field has given me new youth. I am as brisk as I was in India two years ago. The only thing I regret is that the lack of good roads makes it impossible to cover the whole country. For example, for the past three weeks we have been skirting the Arakan-Yoma range, between the Irrawaddy and the Bay of Bengal, without being able to enter it. It's a lofty range covered with elephant-grass, and you can only get about by bullock cart—10 miles a day! . . . You would like jungle travel as much as I do. At the moment it has a rather unusual appearance: some of the trees are beginning to produce pink or yellow blossom, yet the intense dryness has already caused a large-scale shedding of leaves, just as in Auvergne at the end of September . . .

You see, then, how I am spending in the calm of ancient Nature the hours that are so full of tension for China and Europe; and you may well imagine

> that I am not too pleased at being a deserter. Still, I am biding my time—should it ever come—and working patiently to clarify my 'message'(?) and strengthen my platform. It seems to me more important to create a new concept of human activity than to plunge into the feverish intoxication of a political drive which already has its leaders and will never lack followers. At the same time I am watching with great anxiety the strange transmutations we are undergoing but fail to understand. The emancipation of the Far East disturbs me because I have no confidence in the human qualities of the Japanese: they will turn out, I fear, to be false shepherds.[3]

The uneasiness referred to in this letter was as much part of his nature as the devout assurance with which he tackled scientific or moral questions—though whether it arose from impatience at the tangled complexities of modern life or from the mental inhibitions to which his special status as priest-cum-scientist subjected him must, however, remain in doubt. As a scientist, it was his invariable habit to convert energy into activity and track down unsolved problems by dint of strenuous field-work, deriving satisfaction from any discoveries he made. For all its arduousness, scientific research offers moments in which a new pattern suddenly emerges from the chaos of visible phenomena, when fossils and rock formations fall into clear groups and patterns which find a place in the general geological picture. The creative element in such work consists in adapting oneself to the unknown and chaotic. One cannot blame a scientist,

[3] *Letters from a Traveller*, pp. 237-8.

especially a scientist with Teilhard's devout and visionary nature, if the present chaos fills him with a sense of unease and impotence. A humanitarian urge to act, to participate in world events, has always been one of the characteristics of the great scientist. Albert Einstein, Bertrand Russell and, before them, Ernst Haeckel and Alexander von Humboldt have all felt impelled to tackle the crucial problems of their age with the aid of their scientific experience of order and clear powers of perception. However, the world has preferred to dismiss them as visionaries and utopians, and failed to provide them with the facilities worthy of their exalted aspirations. They have been left to watch the inexorable advance of destiny with inward disquiet, to pursue their specialized activities in laboratories and lecture-halls or on voyages of scientific exploration, contenting themselves, as Teilhard did, with hopes of opportunities to come.

However much Teilhard may occasionally have yearned for Peking, I cannot recall that he ever expressed a wish to cut short his stay in Burma. If he had any grounds for impatience, it was due rather to the plans for cave exploration which we had made at the beginning of the year. In accordance with these we drove back to the highlands in the northern Shan States at the end of February, travelling along the completed section of the Burma Road from Mogok to Lashio, in other words, almost to the borders of China's Yunnan Province.[4] In earlier times, the primitive mountain tribes had included some head-hunters, but for all the aboriginal character of the local natives they no longer created a menacing

[4] See also H. de Terra: *The Pleistocene of Burma*, Trans. Am. Phil. Soc., vol. 32, pt 3, 1943.

impression. In fact, there was something more comical than threatening about the short, dark-skinned men and the women with their bizarre metal necklaces.

Although we actually examined a cave containing fossil animal remains, our hopes of more promising finds were soon frustrated by the impassable terrain. The dense mountain forest would have made speedy exploration impossible even if we had possessed adequate transport facilities—and saddle- and pack-animals were unobtainable because caravan traffic on the new Burma Road had stripped neighbouring villages of all available beasts of burden.

One day, when we had driven to the watershed of the Irrawaddy and were looking across at China, Teilhard proposed that instead of wasting more time in this inhospitable district we should return to the Irrawaddy Valley. Before we left Mogok, one of the miners brought us a human mandible which, he said, had come from a cave. When scrutinizing the bone to assess its degree of fossilization, Teilhard employed a test which I had never encountered before. Running his tongue over it, he declared that it was not sufficiently mineralized to count as a fossil because it still retained its original porosity. The way in which he took the bone from the workman's grubby hands and calmly put it to his lips was yet another illustration of the easy-going attitude which made him such an ideal companion on expeditions.

VI

Looking back on our departure from Burma, I must admit that I found it hard to tear myself away, whether because of the idyllic river landscape, the wild expanses of tropical mountain forest, the Buddhist traditions of the country's graceful inhabitants, the colourful splendour of village festivals, or the harmonious and successful way in which we had carried out our researches. Teilhard found it hard to leave, too. 'Our stay in Burma ended satisfactorily. Plenty of interesting results—ancient prehistory and geology. I was sorry to leave the country—I had "adopted" it immediately.'

What no doubt contributed to this favourable impression was the sense of contact with China which Teilhard experienced during our stay in the Shan Hills and which reminded him of his travels in the Chinese interior by donkey caravans. None of us could have predicted that, before long, Burma's age-old towns and peaceful villages would become burnt offerings to the Japanese invader, and that Teilhard would be condemned to seven years of isolation in Peking, but Teilhard's letters imply that he foresaw the immense upheavals which were ultimately to change the face of the Far East so completely.

In the latter half of March, our party assembled in a Rangoon hotel, a place for ever imprinted on my memory by an incident which I recounted to Teilhard on the day of our departure.

At nightfall on the November evening when we had left for the interior, the great port of Rangoon had been engulfed by a cloud of insects. We were standing beside our luggage in the hotel foyer when the place was suddenly filled with whirring creatures, iridescent emerald flies and big black beetles—a veritable inundation of insect bodies which the hotel staff could not sweep away fast enough to keep the way clear. Outside, the street lamps glowed dimly as though through heavy fog, and cars and trams crept laboriously across a pulpy mass of insects' bodies, millions upon millions of them, an entomological apocalypse which threatened to bring urban life to a standstill. I felt less apprehensive than angry at this sudden onslaught, not because it jeopardized our plans for departure but because of man's appalling helplessness in the face of an unexpected invasion by lower forms of life.

One has to have known the tropical world and experienced all its sinister onslaughts on the human body to form an idea of the eternal struggle waged by primitive man against a hostile environment. Were not bears and wolves, mosquitoes and bacilli, floods and volcanic eruptions—all the means employed by Nature to threaten superior forms of life with death or disease—merely a medium for the selection and evolution of new species? Did not the higher consciousness which Teilhard refers to in his writings as the end-product of all evolution serve, from the very outset, like the *coup de poing* of primitive man, as a means of self-preservation?

Teilhard expressed himself on the most burning of all contemporary problems—the survival of civilization and spiritual human values—in an essay entitled *Sauvons l'Humanité*, copies of which he sent to me and other friends before leaving for Burma. I quote a few extracts from it:[1]

> The foundation of all the reactions which current events awaken in our inner selves must be a robust faith in the destiny of Man. Even if that faith is already there, it must be fortified. It is too easy to find an excuse for inaction by pleading the decadence of civilization, or even the imminent end of the world. This defeatism, whether it be innate or acquired, or a mere affectation, seems to me the besetting temptation of our time. . .
>
> Having lived for millenia in self-contradiction, Mankind has now reached a stage of development from which it can, with all its forces, advance *forward*.
>
> It will be objected that, in order finally to constitute a Crusade of Man, there must be an 'antagonist' to oppose. For my part, I do not believe in the supreme effectiveness of the instinct of self-preservation and fear.
>
> It is not the fear of perishing, but the ambition to live which has thrown Man into the exploration of Nature, into the conquest of the ether and the air. The loadstone which must magnetize and purify the energies in us, whose growing surplus is currently dissipated in useless clashes and perverse refinements, I would place, in the last analysis, in the gradual manifestation of some essential object whose total wealth, more precious than gold, more seductive

[1]The following passages are taken from an essay dated 11 November 1936 and published in excerpt form in *Cahiers Pierre Teilhard de Chardin I*, 'Building the Earth', Éditions du Seuil, Paris 1958, pp. 5, 10 et seq.

than any beauty, would be, for Man grown adult, the Grail and Eldorado in which the ancient conquerors believed; something tangible, for the possession of which it would be infinitely good to lay down one's life.

For that reason, if a spiritual Human Front began to come about, it would need, alongside the engineers occupied in organizing the resources and communications of the Earth, other 'technicians' solely concerned with defining and propagating the concrete goals, ever more lofty, upon which the efforts of human activities should be concentrated. Up to now, we have been justifiably keen to unveil the mysteries concealed in matter infinitely great and infinitely small. But an inquiry of much greater importance to the future will be the study of *psychic* currents and attractions; a science of spiritual energy. Perhaps, impelled by the necessity to build the unity of the World, we shall end by perceiving that the great object unwittingly pursued by science is nothing other than the discovery of God.

Teilhard's essay reminds me of an experience I had during our voyage to Java which introduced me to another of his ideas: the concept of a growing cohesion in human energies.

One of our ports of call on the voyage from Rangoon to Singapore was Malacca, where we made a brief stop. Situated on the Malayan coast, on the sea-route between India and China, this port possesses an historical importance associated not only with colonial politics but also, curiously enough, with a saint. I had heard of St Francis Xavier in India because of the Bombay college named after him, where Teilhard had stayed in September 1935. Malacca is like a tropical version of Delft, with tiny gabled houses and narrow streets dating from the time of the Dutch occupation (1641-1824). While still on board, we had noticed a church overlooking the town. After a brief sightseeing tour, we visited it, intrigued by reports that it was a place of Christian pilgrimage, which was the last thing we expected to find in that remote tropical region. It was Teilhard who suggested a visit to the church, which stood silhouetted against the glassy sea in the midday heat like some grotesque crag in an ancient Chinese painting. In view of the torrid humidity, we decided to hire one of the carriages whose drivers and horses were taking a siesta in the shade of the mango-trees.

St Francis Xavier, who was a co-founder of the Jesuit Order in Spain, had established a mission in Malacca shortly after its conquest by the Portuguese under the Duke of Albuquerque. Wherever, in this calm and peaceful bay, Malay kings were venerated or merchants and monks from China and India forgathered, there the Cross was erected under the military aegis of Portuguese adventurers. I imagine that this religious onslaught seemed as tragic to the Malays as its counterpart did to the Aztecs, who were beaten into submission by the Spanish conquistador Cortes at approximately the same period. The history of Christian missionary activity rivalled Islamic proselytism in its ruthless use of political expedients which poured scorn on the religious ethic underlying its evangelical aims. The interesting feature of St Xavier's activities, however, was his vision of a religious conquest of Asia, for he regarded Malacca merely as a springboard or base for his bold plan to convert millions of Chinese and Japanese to the Christian faith. Inspired by a personal sense of apostolic mission, he was really the first Western missionary to challenge the great religions of the Far East since the days of the Nestorian Christians' infiltration into China. What he planned in Malacca was a Napoleonic idea in religious terms. Xavier travelled to Japan and China, where he succumbed to a fever. His mortal remains were buried at Malacca for some time, and because the church there was dedicated to his memory it became a pilgrim's shrine. Inside, we saw natives offering candles and copper coins, much as though the place were the site of some indigenous magic cult.

Mankind has undergone many transformations since the days of Emperor Charles V. We have acquired a better understanding of alien cultures and religions, and our mode of thought has become infinitely freer and less inhibited. We have even started to evolve ideas of human unity or closer association, and the present threat of nuclear war has instilled a sense of responsibility toward mankind. In view of advances like these, who can doubt the rightness of Teilhard's belief in the evolution of human consciousness? The Saint of Malacca may have sensed the necessity for grouping human beings in larger units, but they would, of course, have had to submit to his own religion. He must also have known that no form of unification is practicable without faith in the future. As Teilhard expressed it in one of his essays:[2]

The resources now available to us, the powers we

[2] *Cahiers Pierre Teilhard de Chardin I*, 'Building the Earth', pp. 16-17.

have unleashed, *cannot be absorbed* into the narrow system of individual and national compartments which has so far served the architects of the human earth. *The Age of Nations is past. The task before us now, if we would not perish, is to shake off our ancient prejudices, and to build the Earth.*

The more I look at the World as a scientist *the less I see any other possible biological issue except the active consciousness of its unity.* Life can only progress on our planet in future (and *nothing* will prevent it from progressing, not even its own internal servitudes) by throwing down the barriers which wall off human activity, and by giving itself up without hesitation to Faith in the Future.

We must put in the *forefront* of our *concrete* preoccupations the systematic arrangement and exploration of our Universe, understood as the true country of Mankind. Then material energy will circulate, and, more important still, spiritual energy, corrupted by the petty jealousies of modern society, will find its natural outlet in the attack launched against the mysteries of the World. The time has come to realize that Research is the highest human function. . . .

The organization of elementary human energy must find expression in the fullest possible development of personality.

But today (he wrote in another essay)[3] while the mass formation of the human layer is taking place under our eyes and in our consciousness, Man, assuming him to be henceforward fixed in his

[3] *Cahiers Pierre Teilhard de Chardin I*, 'Building the Earth', p. 21.

> individual nature, can see a new and boundless field of evolution opened up before him; the field of collective creations, associations, ideas and emotions. How can we lay down any limits to the effects of expansion, penetration and spiritual fusion which would flow from the coherent ordering of the human multitude? To dominate and canalize the powers of the air and the sea is all very well. But what is this triumph, compared with the world-wide mastery of human thought and love? In truth, no more magnificent opportunity than this has ever been presented to the hopes and efforts of the Earth.
>
> We are very ready to pride ourselves on living in an age of enlightenment and science. And yet the truth is quite the reverse; we are still bogged down in rudimentary and infantile forms of intellectual conquest. What proportion of activity in the world today, in money, manpower and effort, is devoted to exploring and conquering the still unknown areas of the world?
>
> At present, most men still merely understand strength, the key and symbol of super-being, in its most primitive and savage form: War.

How did Teilhard envisage the realization of human cohesion? In his essay, *Human Energy*, he says:

> The more man becomes a man, the more he senses the need to devote himself to something greater. Isn't that just what we perceive all round us? When, in the Noosphere, has there ever been a more urgent need for the faith and hope required to invest the vast organism which we are constructing with meaning and soul?

He leaves it to human evolution to awaken this total energy and give it an objective. Personality and power of faith are the media through which the process will be effected. Teilhard believed this because 'in the Noosphere, love and thought are in a state of constant growth.'

I can well imagine that, with its historical background, Malacca must have reacted on Teilhard like an historical document. He contemplated it for hours, seeing it as nothing less than a milestone in human evolution and, at the same time, a gauge by which he could assess the transformations that had occurred within his own religious order. Just as the concepts of beauty and goodness have changed in the course of ages, so has the belief in man's higher calling.

All who had the good fortune to spend any time with Teilhard must have become aware how vividly his literary remains evoke his memory, and how stimulating an effect his writings produce by presenting the most trivial incidents in a meaningful light. It is only when recording experiences like these that one realizes that the passing of such a man is not death in the traditional sense, but a reawakening and, indeed, revelation of his influence. It is as though the man who strives for spirituality must die before his legacy to mankind becomes free and creative. In effect, this robs death of its sting, for it marks the beginning of the impact of a spiritual essence which can henceforth operate without corporeal ties.

Considering the grandeur of Teilhard's ideas, I find it strange that I never saw him in the role of preacher or prophet. In my experience, he never made an obtrusively moralizing impression, which was all the more surprising because he was abrim with exalted ideas about the value of personality. On one occasion in Philadelphia, when I was telling him of my own doubts and anxieties in the hope of eliciting some form of clarification from him, his response was more of an appeal to my own ability to find the right road. He seemed content to profess his faith in me, to place his entire reliance on mental energy as the essence of personality. To experience the full impact of his character in this way naturally entailed a certain measure of intimacy and emotional exchange which chance encounters could not have supplied. On such occasions, whether of a professional or purely social nature, he tended to steer conversation towards a subject which arose out of the general discussion but which he pursued with a single-mindedness that admitted of no distraction. Grateful of a chance to speak, he would often be unable to recall the name of the person with whom he had held such a conversation. Even among his intimates he did not, to the best of my knowledge, behave like a prophet of political or social change, but contented himself with looking at things in perspective and thinking constructively where others could only express doubts. Wittingly or unwittingly, he was the founder of a new kind of anthropology, although he would have been hard put to it to find it a home in existing academic institutions.

VII

On 1 April 1938 our party embarked at Singapore in one of the small Dutch steamers which served the Java route. We were nearing an area which might be regarded by students of man's origin as a Promised Land. Java was supplying an exceptional amount of information about various types of human fossils which were geologically distributed throughout the entire Quaternary period. Teilhard's research into the Peking finds had, it was true, disclosed the existence of two types of primitive man, namely, Middle-Quaternary Peking Man and an early form of *Homo sapiens* dating from the Late Quaternary, but the island of Java afforded an opportunity of studying a wide variety of human fossils from the earliest phase of the Quaternary. In reviewing our foregoing studies in India and Burma, we often had occasion to discuss the chronological classification of early human remains. Our forthcoming studies in Java would permit us to draw comparisons between the crucial stratal sequences in Java and those on the Asian mainland, hence our excitement as we awaited our first glimpse of the 'Promised Land'.

Sea-voyages in the tropics create a sense of relaxation, a tendency to surrender oneself to the balmy air and starlit skies of the South. What endowed this short sea-passage with a special quality, however, was the thought that we were gliding across a sort of submerged continent. Beneath the surface lay an ancient topographic relief composed, as oceanographers' soundings have established, of river-beds and hills. The calm and sultry sea lies like a smooth coverlet over the geological drama, the explosive volcanoes, the imperceptibly growing coral reefs and crustal disturbances which are typical of the whole Sunda archipelago. In the time of the earliest men the Java Sea was a neck of dry land linking the Malayan mainland with the islands of today. Created by a fall in the sea-level due to glaciation, this causeway had encouraged the spread of animal and human life. How else could *Pithecanthropus*, the best-known of all Java's fossil men, have reached the island, and how else could land animals have been found in company with a man whose fossil remains bear the closest resemblance to others found in India and China? This land-bridge provided a sizeable area of operations for the primitive men whom Teilhard's book on the origin of man placed in the 'ramificatory phase' of early human evolution.[1] Thus, our voyage across the submerged causeway could be envisaged as a sort of geological introduction or prologue to our expedition to Java. The island and its rich fossil sites were not new to Teilhard, of course, since he had made a most valuable trip there with Dr von Koenigswald two years before. On his return to Peking he wrote his friend and host a letter, dated February 1936, parts of which I should like to reproduce here because they indicate the keen interest with which Teilhard followed the progress of palaeontological research in Java at this period.[2]

[1] *Le Groupe zoölogique humain*, p. 91.
[2] Unpublished letter dated 11 February 1936 from the archives of the Fondation Teilhard de Chardin, Paris.

> My dear Koenigswald,
> I arrived in Peiping only a few days ago, and have had no time until now to write a few lines to thank you for the glorious days I spent with you. We are now friends for always.
>
> On arrival here I at once wrote a long letter to Merriam (Carnegie Institution), commending you and your research to the Carnegie Institution in the warmest terms. I hope it will yield results. Up here, we are still in the dark as to the prospects of financial support for the Cenozoic Laboratory[3] from the Rockefeller Foundation, so Weidenreich cannot yet say anything about possible support for you (or about his own trip to Java). Things should be clearer by the beginning of March, and I will immediately write and tell you what we can do. Chapman Andrews (leader of the expedition sponsored by New York Museum) intends to come to Peiping early next year. I will then discuss with him personally the question of the diggings to be undertaken in Java with your help.

Another passage in the same letter is very typical of the manner in which Teilhard used to impart professional advice to his colleagues:

> Concentrate mainly on factual observations. Scientists prefer facts rather than personal interpretations.

His wide experience had taught him that, in the case of major pioneering work carried out in remote areas, accurate documentation was of paramount importance.

[3] Dr Franz Weidenreich, the celebrated anatomist, had been appointed to succeed Dr Davidson Black as director of this research institute, which concentrated on the study of fossil man in China with the support of the Rockefeller Foundation.

What adds to the interest of the foregoing excerpts from the point of view of our trip to Java is the fact that, a year before the conference in Philadelphia, Teilhard had established contact with the scientific institute in question, the Carnegie Institution, whose president, Dr John C. Merriam, had sponsored my own research in India. I clearly recollect, too, a discussion I had with Dr Andrews of the American Museum of Natural History in New York in 1939, relating to the large-scale excavations that would undoubtedly have taken place in Java if the outbreak of the Second World War had not prevented such a promising venture.

When our boat berthed at Batavia on 3 April, Dr von Koenigswald was waiting on the quay to greet us. I suppose I did not realize at the time how brief Teilhard's stay in Java was destined to be. In actuality, he was thinking of returning to Peking within a fortnight, as the following letter dated 5 April implies:

> We arrived at Batavia the day before yesterday, and I am staying, just as I did two years ago, with my friend von Koenigswald in Bandung. It was he who six months ago had the good fortune to find the second *Pithecanthropus* skull. The rains are nearly over and in consequence I can see the fine ring of volcanoes standing out against a clearer sky than in 1936. . . . I leave Batavia on the 16th and travel by the excellent Messageries (Félix Roussel) which should get me to Shanghai on the 25th. . . .
>
> Java is really an ideal country. I am just back from an expedition to an active volcano whose summit (crater) can be reached by car. The summit is covered with virgin forest, the lower slopes with

tea and cinchona: luxury hotels along the road, bungalows with swimming pools. I prefer the real jungle—still, there's something very pleasant about this artificial beauty.[4]

He had arrived in Java only two days before, found it an ideal country and was looking forward to some interesting excursions from Bandung under the expert guidance of Dr von Koenigswald, yet his passage to China was already booked. Perhaps he had received alarming accounts of the Japanese occupation of Peking and felt that the uncertainty of his position there justified his premature departure.

On the very day following our arrival we gained some idea of Java's profusion of primitive human types. An assistant of Dr W. F. F. Oppenoorth showed us the eleven *Homo soloensis* skulls which the latter had unearthed between 1932 and 1937. I can still see Teilhard standing beside the table on which this remarkable series lay spread out, discussing each specimen with Dr von Koenigswald and drawing attention to certain noteworthy features which appeared to bear a resemblance to Java Man. What seemed particularly important to him, however, was to ascertain the geological age of the formation from which the fossils had been disinterred, together with huge quantities of animal remains and numerous stone tools. Nothing would have been more satisfying to me, as a geologist, than the solution of this question. Our present visit to Java aimed at clarifying geological occurrences which could bring us a closer understanding of human evolution. Accurate checking of comparative dates seemed all the more important

[4] *Letters from a Traveller*, pp. 239-40.

because the various human fossils which were older than Solo Man had been collected by natives and were not the result of systematic excavation. Lastly, it is as important to the palaeontologist and prehistorian to know the exact location and stratigraphy of such finds as it is to an archaeologist. Without a precise knowledge of the caves in which local inhabitants came across the 'Dead Sea Scrolls' and without having excavated neighbouring ruins, we should still be in the dark as to their origin.

Let no one cherish any false illusions about the thoroughness of Teilhard's scientific research. Despite his tendency to synthesize and classify facts under wider headings and in broader perspective, he always insisted on accurate observation. He showed the most meticulous care in this respect—or so it seemed to me during our joint research in India and Burma, areas which were virgin territory from his point of view.

The fact that Teilhard combined this analytical and critical faculty with a philosophical, profoundly religious and, one might almost say, mystical disposition will always remain one of my deepest and most abiding impressions. It is so rare to find an interest in philosophy among scientists that Teilhard's genius seems doubly unique, for it was a genius in which all scientific knowledge gravitated toward a goal which might be described as a manifestation of Goethe's '*Gottnatur*'. The true genius is a human phenomenon whose structure, like a mosaic, creates a harmonious picture out of the most antithetical components. It has its own domain and its own laws, which must be respected. The realm of genius is neither supermundane nor inframundane, but probably lies in a special sphere of energies of a kind which remains undisclosed to us unless we are drawn into the orbit of a man of genius.

Much as I may have succumbed to the spell of Teilhard's personality, time has erased the day-to-day events of our trip to Java from my memory, leaving behind only isolated impressions. One of these is of an excursion into the island's interior to visit various sites which had yielded fossil human remains. From Bandung we travelled to Surakarta, ancient seat of the Javanese princes, where we watched dancers rehearsing for a performance in the palace. It was like some old oriental fairy-tale, with young dancing-girls in heavy brocaded costumes gliding beneath the mango-trees in the palace courtyard to the strains of a gamelang orchestra, like so many enchanted princesses. From this scene of ancient splendour our route took us to the site of Java Man's discovery at Trinil, where the Dutch doctor Eugene Dubois made his sensational find in 1891.

Among the photographs which I took on this trip is one which shows Teilhard standing next to Dr von Koenigswald, his face hot and flushed beneath his tropical helmet, looking at the memorial to Dr Dubois, a former pupil of Ernst Haeckel at Jena. Dubois was the only one of Haeckel's students who took the idea of man's descent from the ape seriously enough to devote the best years of his life to a quest for the fossil remains of a 'missing link'. After years of research he found the relics of *Pithecanthropus* exactly where Haeckel's teachings suggested they might be: in the tropics, where the natives had given a jungle ape the name *orang-outang*, or 'forest man'. For a moment, the memorial seemed to reawaken the violent disputes which had raged between conflicting schools of scientific opinion in his day, disputes which had furnished the anti-clerical factions with such controversial arguments at about the turn of the century. Since then, prehistoric research had come of age and developed into a scientific field of its own. It will always be one of the outstanding features of my voyages of scientific exploration that I was privileged to see two of its most distinguished adepts together in that memorable place.

Fortunately, this site of discovery and others of its kind are situated in one of Java's dry zones, where the search for fossil remains is not hampered by tropical rain-forest. However, we soon gained an idea of the difficulties involved in such field-work when Dr von Koenigswald took us to the place where *Homo soloensis* had been found—on the River Solo near the village of Ngandong. This was where Oppenoorth discovered the skulls which we had been shown in Batavia, embedded in a volcanic formation that had accumulated by the action of rain and streams. Almost three thousand bones belonging to land animals (vertebrates) had been unearthed during the excavations, and it was to be assumed that the artefacts which Teilhard and Movius collected so laboriously that day—scrapers, knives and other tools—came from strata of a similar age. Throughout the hot and sultry day, our party gathered specimens and discussed the stratigraphy of the site. We were to spend the night in a thatched hut, and looked forward with some eagerness to a well-earned rest, especially as a strenuous tour was planned for the morrow. Teilhard stretched out next to me on one of the beds, a primitive affair consisting of a straw mat mounted on a wooden frame. It was impossible to undress properly because some of the village elders insisted on stationing themselves inside the hut or at the open doorways, smoking, chattering and watching our attempts at slumber with interest. It may have been a local way of honouring guests, but what with the mosquitoes, which were undeterred from sipping our blood by the smell of cigar smoke, and the village dogs, which barked incessantly, sleep was quite out of the question. Next morning, Teilhard declared that he felt sufficiently rested to join the proposed excursion on foot along the river-bank. We had the choice of travelling downstream by boat or of following a path which would eventually bring us to a main road. Since my restless night had not helped me to digest my rice supper properly, and breakfast had consisted of a few bananas, the prospect of a day's march through tropical forest did not seem particularly alluring. Teilhard showed no signs of discomfort, however, so we set off.

Our march, which I shall never forget, took us along a narrow path in the hot and humid shade of huge bamboo thickets which occasionally afforded a glimpse of the river. Isolated bird-calls broke the stillness of the tropical forest. Knowing Teilhard's predilection for such sounds, I imagine that he must have been enjoying himself as he walked along ahead of me, but as soon as the path became swampy our mood of enjoyment vanished. Each step took us further into a black morass of glutinous, clayey mud which rose above our ankles. I saw Teilhard trudging ahead with bowed head. Like ours, his shirt was soaked with sweat and his khaki slacks encrusted with mud, but his tennis-shoes, which several times came off in the mud, proved an added hardship. Bathed in sweat, we waded through the stifling forest. The dense undergrowth precluded our making any detours, and we had to pick our way across particularly marshy stretches with the utmost care. We began to regret having come on foot, and reflected ruefully how much easier it would have been to make the trip by river. Finally, at midday, we reached a small group of huts, where we sank exhausted on to a tree-stump and drank cool milk from some coconuts which the natives brought us from neighbouring palm-trees. I cannot remember how we managed to persevere with our excruciating march throughout the rest of the afternoon, but we eventually reached a settlement and continued our journey by car and train. The few snapshots I took during the march confirm my recollection of Teilhard's exhausted condition. But, although fatigue had robbed his whole figure of its wonderful poise and his face betrayed physical exhaustion, not a word of criticism or complaint escaped his lips.

When we said goodbye to Teilhard in mid-April, no one apart from him could have had the remotest inkling how great a part his scientific observations in South-East Asia would play in helping him to formulate his ideas on the origin of man. His second visit to Java was to be particularly instrumental in conveying a clear picture of the phylogenetic ramification of the prehominids in Asia. We had inspected the site of the Modjokerto fossil, geologically the oldest, as well as that of *Pithecanthropus* and *Homo soloensis*, and we had daily exchanged ideas on their comparative ages and geological significance. Teilhard was thus in a position to gauge the true importance of Dr von Koenigswald's subsequent findings. In Teilhard's view, the fossil types found in Java belong, together with Peking Man and the outsize forms *Meganthropus* and *Gigantopithecus*, to an 'off-shoot' of the human race which is represented by similar forms in Africa.[5] Thanks to his high degree of familiarity with extinct forms of the human genus found in East and South Asia, subsequent studies in South Africa enabled him to form a general picture of human evolution. Its divergence from other hypothetical family trees lies in the fact that Teilhard assigned the earlier species a place outside the main stem or axis of human evolution. Whereas all the early species were subject to a rapid differentiation which resulted in their extinction, man proper evolved independently of them into the sole surviving species. The merit of this theory as opposed to other hypotheses is that it explains the antiquity of the *Homo sapiens* type, which dates back to the Middle Quaternary. The latter's age makes it difficult to classify it as a descendant of contemporaneous types, like Java and Peking Man, so Teilhard's theory neatly disposes of the necessity for a 'missing link' or bridge between man and ape. Teilhard's writings repeatedly stress the uniqueness of human evolution, on the grounds that in the course of the last two million years 'Nature has witnessed the emergence of no really new group apart from the hominids.'

Teilhard held that the *Homo sapiens* type, which appeared about half way through the Quaternary period, denoted a reversal in the evolution of the hominids in that divergence, or division into separate groups, gave

[5] *Le Groupe zoölogique humain*, p. 83 et seq., also Fig. 5 on p. 91, which illustrates phylogenic relationships diagrammatically.

way to convergence. This marked the development of the *noosphere*, or layer of consciousness, which evolved from the *biosphere* concomitantly with the rapid spread of *Homo sapiens*. Teilhard assumed the 'focal point' of this final and most significant phase to be in Africa, since that is where the earliest traces of *Homo faber*, the tool-maker, are to be found.

When considering Teilhard's idea of the geographical location of this 'focal point', we should remember that such hypotheses depend on completeness of documentation. In Africa's case, brilliant and diligent research by individual scholars has elicited information about ancient forms of *Homo sapiens* which are still lacking in the case of Asia. Must we therefore dismiss the other alternative suggested by the fossils found in South and East Asia? Could the appearance of 'conscious' man not just as well have occurred in South-East Asia, where Teilhard himself saw a 'pronounced centre' of the spread of the *Pithecanthropus* group? Eminent palaeontologists have, after all, assumed the emergence of new ungulates and primates in Asia, and Central Asia in particular, during the Tertiary. I believe that we must wait for further information before accepting the validity of Teilhard's thesis that man originated in Africa.

A similar lacuna in existing knowledge affects another of Teilhard's ideas, namely, that there is a universal geological period enclosing the earliest palaeolithic tools, which are, in default of other signs of human intelligence, to be associated with the emergence of 'conscious' man. Teilhard dated this frontier in the Middle Quaternary. Although this period, which lasted for more than a hundred thousand years, has yielded indisputable archaeological evidence of the existence of *Homo faber*, who, as the sites of Peking Man's discovery demonstrate, was also familiar with the use of fire, research since carried out in China and East Africa has unearthed artefacts from far older geological strata. The fossil skull of *Zinjanthropus*, discovered in the Oldoway gorge in Tanganyika in summer 1959, may be regarded as the earliest evidence of the artefact-producing culture known as the Oldowan, which is geologically dated at the very beginning of the Quaternary or even the close of the Tertiary.[6] This means that the very earliest men, and not only those known to us from the Middle Quaternary, can be regarded as tool-makers. But who can say with any certainty that the phenomenon of human consciousness can be perceived in these earliest artefacts? The number and diversity of the oldest palaeolithic cultures may at best be regarded as symptoms of a new phase in the development of primeval intelligence—although even this seems presumptuous, since stone artefacts may have been preceded by artefacts made of other materials, such as bone or hardwood, which are less durable than stone. In view of such uncertainties, no definite conclusions can yet be formed about Teilhard's 'focal centre' of consciousness, though it is quite apparent from his writings that he saw it not as a chance occurrence but as a sort of 'psychical mutation'.

A better understanding of this concept demands some further insights into Teilhard's world of ideas, of which something will be said in the following chapter.

[6] L. S. B. Leakey, *Adam's Ancestors*, Harper Bros, New York 1960, *IX* and *X*. Preliminary dating by radiation measurement yielded an age of about 1,750,000 years, which would correspond to the Pliocene age.

VIII

If a perceptive scholar like Teilhard found his first visit to the sites of fossil man's discovery in Java 'fateful', as he mentions in one of his letters, it may be imagined how much importance he attached to his existing scientific ideas.[1] What, in fact, was so fateful about this trip? The concept of convergence in the evolution of the human race was so essential to Teilhard's account of man's origin that it is easy to understand why he was so greatly encouraged in that idea by his new-found knowledge of extinct types of primitive man in Java. With the disappearance of typal diversity within the Java and Peking Man group, modern man emerged as the sole surviving species and the one which dominated the entire world. What others regard as a chance phenomenon of survival became, for Teilhard, a manifestation of some deeper meaning underlying the evolution of man.

After his second trip to Java, one might thus have expected him to record his findings in a paper dealing with the zoological status of man and incorporating his newly acquired impressions. It was doubly surprising, therefore, when he reported from Peking four months later that he had started on the first chapter of his book *Le Phénomène humain*, which was to be concerned less with evolution than with presenting a general picture of the physical universe. It was evidently envisaged as a *magnum opus* and not as a palaeontological evaluation of his

[1] *Letters from a Traveller*, p. 218 et seq.

studies of early man. On 5 August 1938 he wrote that 'plan and inspiration' for the above-named work had matured sufficiently, indicating that he had already been contemplating the project for some time.

The assurance with which he approached the grand panorama of man's existence seems to me to have a bearing on his attitude toward science. Had on-the-spot observations been the sole factors governing the formulation of his theory on the 'hominization' of the life-force, he would first have turned to the subject of man's origin. I have already mentioned in a previous chapter that Teilhard's scientific work gave the impression that he had already formulated his ideas and was only waiting for external observation to prove them well-founded. Although it is the distinguishing characteristic of all inspiration to hurry on ahead of scientific evidence, one is bound, in Teilhard's case, to remember his visionary disposition, which was rooted in religious faith. His vision of the common destiny of mankind had become so much of a mission with him that new scientific data had to take second place.

Teilhard was a unique blend of personal revelation and scientific experience. Before I yield to the temptation to look for similar instances in natural science, I should first say a few words about my last meetings with Teilhard.

When I next saw him in New York in the summer of 1939, he spoke of the philosophical evaluation of his studies, to which he intended to devote his whole energies. During a brief joint visit to Harvard we discussed the possibility of further research in Asia with one or two professional colleagues, but prospects did not seem bright. From there Teilhard travelled back, via California, to Peking, where he at once resumed work on his *magnum opus*.

The fact that he was able to write this work in Peking, far removed from the tribulations of the Second World War, may be regarded as a special dispensation of Providence. The first half of his manuscript was finished by January 1940, and the provisional draft was completed a few months later. He was simultaneously engaged on palaeontological studies which ultimately led to the formation of a study group which he christened the 'Institute of Geo-Biology'. Since the Japanese occupation of North China precluded any form of field-work, Teilhard was able to concentrate more than ever upon laboratory work and literary commitments. It was at this period that he asked me to contribute to the journal of his new institute, a request which I at once fulfilled by sending him a longish essay on China's Quaternary geology and its relationship to that of India.

Ten years were to pass before I saw Teilhard again in New York. It was late autumn of 1954 when I had a last opportunity of discussing the problems of human evolution with him. We met at the Wenner-Gren Foundation for Anthropological Research, where a work-room had been placed at his disposal. With the Foundation's support, he was applying himself to the study of fossil man in Africa, which recent findings encouraged him to regard as the scene of modern man's first appearance. This was why he was interested in my plan to search for traces of early man in Spain, which I hoped would shed some light on certain features of

African prehistory. Although he would have preferred me to have chosen Africa rather than Spain he seconded my proposal to the Foundation, which had generously assisted my earlier researches in Mexico.

Teilhard took a lively interest in studies of African prehistory at this period, but he was devoting most of his energies to a philosophical evaluation of his own research. Thus, the paper which he contributed to the international congress due to be held at Princeton University in 1955 dealt with the age and spread of cultures. Immediately after his death at Easter of the same year, Teilhard's spiritual testament became available in the shape of a wide range of publications, of which *The Phenomenon of Man* may be regarded as the most important. Although, in common with his other writings, it supplies information about his scientific findings, the foregoing account will have made it clear that his objectives lay far beyond the traditional domain of natural science. One finds it all the more surprising to read, in a preface to the book in question, that Teilhard requests his readers to regard it 'not as a work on metaphysics, still less as a sort of theological essay, but purely and simply as a scientific treatise.' Yet how, in view of Teilhard's twin hypotheses (that man's importance in Nature is paramount and that his destiny is organically determined), could he have embarked on an all-embracing treatment of the Universe on a purely rational basis and without reference to the belief which he espoused as a member of a respected religious order? It was only to be expected that, as a believer and a scientist, Teilhard would qualify his conception of science. This he did in his own way by commending *seeing* and *contemplation* as aids to a deeper understanding of the human being. His new conception of man was meant to convey a realization 'that he is not an isolated unit lost in the cosmic solitudes' but that a 'universal will to live converges and is hominized in him.'[2]

A study of Teilhard's rich mosaic of writings soon demonstrates that his ultimate concern was for a scientifically based belief in man, and that he used his scientific studies to buttress this faith in man's high calling. By straying from the path traditionally trodden by science, which focusses upon facts, he laid himself open to a charge of having linked two incompatibles, faith and science. This charge can justifiably be levelled at him only if one adheres to the conventional idea of science. As soon as one examines the history of the natural sciences, however, one discovers that their terms of reference have not always been the same. Various scientists have lent them a special character, and some of the most eminent among them have evaluated their findings ideologically in order to arrive at a cosmic synthesis. Although it might be worth-while to draw comparisons between Teilhard's approach and that of others, this can only be attempted on a limited scale in the present work. Since I have set out to record personal recollections and impressions, I shall here confine myself to the scientists who happened to figure in my conversations with Teilhard.

Having embarked on a study of Alexander von Humboldt two years before Teilhard's death, I had occasion to discuss Humboldt's *Kosmos* with him. Needless to say, he was not unaware that this distinguished friend

[2] *The Phenomenon of Man*, p. 36.

and contemporary of Goethe had striven to formulate an idea of cosmic unity which would endow man with a sense of direction.

'The thoughtful scientist's most important achievement,' says Humboldt, 'is, therefore, this: to recognize unity in diversity, to comprehend all that the discoveries of recent times tell us about the individual, to sift and scrutinize details without succumbing beneath their weight, and, *mindful of man's high destiny, to perceive the spirit of Nature*, which lies hidden beneath a covering of external phenomena. In this way, *our endeavours will reach beyond the narrow confines of the external world* and we shall succeed in mastering the raw material of empirical observation, as it were, by ideas.'[3]

Despite Humboldt's attempts to avoid indulging in 'natural philosophy' in *Kosmos*, his *Ansichten der Natur* and certain passages in his correspondence make it very clear that he tried to understand Nature not only in terms of measurement and analysis, as Schiller once unjustly alleged, but sensing it to be filled with an all-pervading spiritual force. In this context, he wrote: 'In the forests of the River Amazon, as on the crest of the High Andes, I realized how, from pole to pole, as though *animated by a single breath, one life alone* is diffused among stones, plants, animals and in the swelling breast of man.'[4] To Humboldt, the unity of the cosmos was a manifestation of inner contemplation and a pantheistic approach to life. His conception of 'Nature, in the manifold meaning of the word, now as a totality of being and

[3] *Kosmos, Entwurf einer physischen Weltbeschreibung*, J. G. Cotta, Stuttgart and Tübingen, 1845, Vol. I, p. 6.

[4] Letter dated 14 May 1806 to Karoline von Wolzogen.

becoming, now as the mysterious archetype of all external phenomena' and his striving for a higher degree of awareness in understanding the cosmos seem to bear an affinity to Teilhard's *seeing* and *contemplation*, just as it does to Goethe's *Gottnatur*. Thus, the numinous manner in which Teilhard couples *experience* of Nature with scientific *knowledge* of Nature is not as novel as it at first appears. What distinguishes his position from that of others is that he pursued the 'mysterious archetype of all external phenomena' scientifically, and not merely as a visionary or man of faith. This is where comparisons with other scientists of philosophical bent derive their especial interest, since they yield insights into the relationship between science and religion, which Teilhard's work presented in such a significant light.

When one remembers Humboldt's recourse to the medium of receptive contemplation as an aid to comprehending the unity of the cosmos, one appreciates how diametrically opposed it was to the mechanistic theory of life espoused by his contemporary Laplace or to the scientific approach of Darwin, who never felt impelled to contemplate life in cosmic terms. Humboldt died in 1859, a few months before the publication of Darwin's major work. The latter's appearance ushered in a new epoch in biological theory and has led, in our own day, to a realization that human evolution represents a special case within the general evolution of life. Because the zoological group known as hominids became differentiated within what was, geologically, a relatively short space of time, and because it ultimately produced *Homo sapiens*—whether unsystematically and by accident or, in Teilhard's idiom, by a 'hominization of the life-force'—

the process of organic development was given a twist which is entirely unique in Nature. Endowed with reason and intellect, this creature has become the object of a novel type of research in which biology shares the field with new branches of learning grouped under the heading of psychology. It was certainly no accident that Sigmund Freud embarked on his studies just when Ernst Haeckel was turning Darwinian theory into a philosophy of life.

To mention Haeckel's name in an essay on Teilhard may seem odd, when one recalls the violent attacks made by that eminent father of modern zoology on religious institutions and theology in general. Yet, for all his attacks on the Church and Christian dogma, Haeckel himself found it necessary to establish a new sort of religion in order to grasp the meaning of evolution. His 'monism' was designed to bridge the gap between science and religion.[5] Two features of Haeckel's ideas are of interest in relation to Teilhard: first the concept of inanimate particles (variously referred to as monads or atoms) to which he denied consciousness; and, second, his assumption that psychical energy evolved in the course of the world's history into the conscious being. Teilhard's train of reasoning is reminiscent of Haeckel's conception of cerebral development in mammals, whose brain-pans increased some six- or eight-fold during the Tertiary period. 'The peculiar natural phenomenon

[5] Monism is the doctrine of animate or energy-laden particles of matter which, inherent in simple protoplasmic organisms, are subject to continuous evolution. 'On the contrary, we hold, with Goethe, that "matter cannot exist and be operative without spirit, nor spirit without matter".' (Ernst Haeckel: *The Riddle of the Universe*, Thinker's Library, London 1929, pp. 17, 173 et seq.)

of consciousness,' wrote Haeckel, 'is a physiological and neurological problem', and again: 'the psyche is a collective term for the whole of the psychical functions of plasms . . . the psychical activities of sensation and will are latent in the smallest structures.'

Compare Teilhard: 'Since everything *in the Universe*, starting from Man, takes place *in the personalized being*, the ultimate Term of the universal Convergence must also possess (in the supreme degree) the quality of a Person. *To super-animate*, *without destroying*, a Universe made up of personal elements, he must himself be a special Centre. Thus reappears, no longer instinctive but closely linked with contemporary ideas on evolution, the traditional conception of a God exerting an intellectual influence upon immortal monads, distinct from himself. . . . In the first place—before Man—the attraction was vitally, but blindly, felt by the World. Since Man, it is awakened, at least partially, in reflective liberty, and it sustains Religion. . . . Religion represents the long unfolding, through the collective experience of all Mankind, of the existence of God—God reflecting himself personally on the organized sum of thinking monads, to guarantee a sure issue, and to lay down exact laws for their hesitant activities.'[6]

The concept of the monad, which goes back to Leibnitz, here appears in the form of an evolutionary doctrine which differs entirely from Haeckel's philosophy of life. Monism was based on a purely mechanistic idea of the evolution of life. In this, man was regarded in Darwinian terms as having evolved from the primates by a process

[6] *Cahiers Pierre Teilhard de Chardin I*, 'Building the Earth' ('The Spirit of Earth') pp. 18-19.

of natural selection, and Haeckel left it to future research to unearth fossil transitional species, half way between man and ape. According to him, man was a chance product of evolution, and because evidence of the diversity of primitive forms of man was lacking in his day he could not regard the evolution of the human species as a special case.[7] But can the creature endowed with reasoning power have come into being accidentally, when its existence was a prerequisite of any understanding of Nature? It is Teilhard's great achievement to have supplied a new answer to this question. To him, the special circumstances surrounding our appearance on earth acquire meaning only if man is regarded as a logical manifestation of psychical forces which gradually condense into consciousness by a sort of 'mutation'. Did Teilhard mean to suggest that anthropogenesis is the logical outcome of a process of psychical evolution which follows rules of its own—rules to which, in analogy with biological knowledge, we can attribute genetic features? In this connexion, reference must briefly be made to discoveries made since Teilhard's death which have shed new light on the origin of man. The fossils found in East Africa (1959) and Italy (1958) indicate that the human race is very much older than even Teilhard could have supposed. Similarly, preliminary studies of the fossil skeleton of *Oreopithecus*, a specimen of the higher Pliocene primates, found in a coal seam, have disclosed that a form of specialization existed within this group

[7] Suggested analogies between Haeckel's and Teilhard's ideas are therefore confined entirely to conceptions of an energy underlying matter and of its gradual evolution.

several million years ago.[8] Whether the creature in question was an early member of the human race proper, as assumed by its discoverer, the Swiss palaeontologist Dr J. Hürzeler, and others, or a species of ape which aspired to humanity, it can certainly be regarded as one—if not the critical—manifestation of the process which Teilhard invested with a capacity for 'mutations'. In as much as the case of *Oreopithecus* raises the question of whether the human race evolved independently of the other primates, one is reminded of the original ideas propounded in a sensational book published almost thirty years ago by the palaeontologist Edgar Dacqué of Munich, whose lectures I once attended. I well remember discussing Dacqué's views on the origin of man with Teilhard, who showed a keen interest in them. They were based on the strange conception of an evolutionary trend which has, in the course of geological epochs, and by a gradual shedding of animal characteristics, caused the human being to emerge from an animal-man community. Myths and legends are supposed to help us recognize 'primeval recollections' of the intimate relationship between man and beast in human evolution.[9]

Just as Dacqué's work ultimately deserted the realm of scientific palaeontological research in favour of a natural philosophy with religious undertones, so (like Teilhard) he dismissed the concept of a mechanical process of human evolution. To Dacqué, contemplation and seeing as media of anthropological understanding

[8] In 1956 the author collaborated with Dr J. Hürzeler on geological studies in the province of Tuscany which paved the way for this discovery.

[9] Edgar Dacqué: *Urwelt, Sage und Menschheit. Eine naturhistorisch-metaphysische Studie*, R. Oldenbourg, Munich, 3rd ed., 1925, p. 13.

were just as important as faith.[10] The following passage from his book is strongly reminiscent of Teilhard:

> The old factual research will survive; it has proved its worth in its own field, and without it our intellect will achieve nothing. But it will be joined by an inner contemplation which stems from self-inquiry and a knowledge of the 'interior of Nature'. We ourselves are that 'interior'. Human nature is the gauge and essence of material objects . . . from it stems our knowledge of them, both inwardly from contemplation and outwardly from the empiricism of the senses.[11]

Just as Teilhard's contemplation of man in the cosmos brought him a spiritual contentment which others were to share, so Dacqué believed that 'we are entering a period in which we, as scientists, will soon not only have to worry about the "spiritual welfare" of our adepts but automatically see in it the spiritual purpose of our own, and possibly all, research. There are objective and intuitive symptoms of this.' To Teilhard and Dacqué alike, research entailed an ethical attitude and deep sense of personal responsibility toward others which made an unforgettable impression on all who were in daily contact with them.

Only personal experience can convey the limitations

[10] In Dacqué's case, it is worth noting that he came of a Protestant Huguenot family and was not a church-going believer.

[11] Compare Teilhard: 'I categorically refuse to apply the mechanical process of selection crudely to the case of man.' (*Nouvelles Lettres de Voyage*, 1939-1955, Grasset, Paris 1957, p. 51.) And again: 'The time has come to realize that an interpretation of the universe—even a positivistic one—remains unsatisfying unless it covers the interior, as well as the exterior, of things; mind as well as matter.' (*The Phenomenon of Man*, pp. 35-6.)

imposed on any understanding of questions concerning man's place in Nature by exclusive concentration on the bare bones of factual science. If one couples Teilhard's lofty conception of research and the revelations arising from it with the experience of other thinkers and seers, it strengthens one's conviction that the quest for knowledge springs from a religious need. This was the opinion of the greatest scientist of our age, Albert Einstein, when he expressed these relationships in the classic words:

> But science can only be created by those who are thoroughly imbued with the aspiration towards truth and understanding. This source of feeling, however, springs from the sphere of religion. To this there also belongs the faith in the possibility that the regulations valid for the world of existence are rational, that is, comprehensible to reason. I cannot conceive of a genuine scientist without that profound faith. The situation may be expressed by an image: science without religion is lame, religion without science is blind.[12]

IX

No account of my experiences with Teilhard de Chardin would be complete without a reference to something which imbued his scientist's nature with a special quality: the fact that it was activated by a pronounced sense of happiness. Therein lay the essential vigour of his character, which never lost its spiritual elasticity, even

[12] Albert Einstein: *Out of my later years*, Thames and Hudson, London 1950, p. 29.

under the pressure of momentous events. Self-evident as it may seem that genuine dedication to an idea or a belief brings happiness, it is rare for it to impart the sort of vigour which Teilhard possessed to so marked a degree. Erudition and the spirit of inquiry do not invariably confer happiness on their possessors; on the contrary, there have been many great scientists whose discoveries have depressed rather than elated them. The degree to which Teilhard found happiness in his research is evident from his personal impact on others and, more especially, in his urge to expatiate upon the various kinds of happiness.

I am thinking in particular of a conversation during which I expressed some doubts about the value of our work. Political developments seemed to indicate that a world-wide catastrophe was imminent, and I felt that our explorations in Burma resembled the burrowing of so many blind moles. Teilhard at once raised my spirits by remarking that as long as we were helping to increase man's knowledge of man, and could look upon it as an adventure, we ought to be of good cheer. It was a special privilege, he said, to be conscious of our share in the growth of the life surrounding us.

The importance which Teilhard attached to defining his sense of happiness and conveying it to others is apparent from a small monograph devoted exclusively to this particular subject.[1] Happiness, Teilhard believed, is generally experienced in three forms:

(i) *In tranquillity:* by not indulging in undue risks or exertions, avoiding all unpleasantnesses as far as possible

[1] *Cahiers Pierre Teilhard de Chardin* II, 'Réflexions sur le bonheur'. Éditions du Seuil, Paris 1960, pp. 57-8.

and restricting emotion, thought and desire to a minimum.

(ii) *In pleasure:* by living profitably but without genuinely creative endeavour, trimming one's sails to the wind and being alert to the advantages of the moment.

(iii) *In growth:* a pleasure which emerges, without really being anticipated, as a by-product of conscious participation in any constructive activity which is devoted to a greater goal.

It goes without saying that Teilhard devoted himself to the latter category of experience, but how exactly did he envisage it? He would hardly have been content with the modern hedonism which he found prevalent among the intellectuals of his day. His scientific research was motivated not solely by curiosity, but by an inner longing to share in the evolution of personal awareness, which has now reached a critical phase. I have already indicated the nature of this evolution. The sum total of life, whose energies are pressing forward with ever-increasing momentum in a predetermined direction, has undergone particular intensification and refinement in man. The repercussions of this process are apparent primarily in science and technology, but also in the social and political realm. We are involved in a continuum of mental activity, not like driftwood floating passively in a river but as repositories of pulsating energy and actively creative components.

This notion is attractive and agreeable enough in itself, but Teilhard deemed it necessary to regard the vast process that is going on within the zoological group called man as confirmation of his theory of a 'convergence' of psychical energies which it will take geological epochs to complete. One can approve of this view and still question whether it is absolutely essential to the third form of happiness (that is, participation in growing personal consciousness). In my opinion, an understanding of the special nature of human evolution and of the ethical responsibilities accruing from it to the individual should suffice to provide us with inner contentment.

Teilhard's summons is like a clarion call: 'Let us unflinchingly join the vanguard of those who are ready to risk the climb to the summit. *En avant!*'

In other words, let the weary and the pessimists stay behind and the hedonists rest on the mountainside: true happiness consists in climbing, in pressing on toward the summit. In a certain sense, each can be his own explorer, for it is the task of each to find the right way to the best summit. Where are the guides, if not within ourselves?

The fact that we still know far too little about man should not deter us from keeping our gaze fixed on three potential ways of realizing a supreme sense of happiness.

First, there is cultivation of the individual, which Teilhard termed *centration*, a conscious striving from the moral and spiritual aspect rather than the purely physical. The harder we work at perfecting ourselves, the greater our influence on the momentum and direction of the general 'flow'. We must constantly endeavour to adapt our individual existence to fit personal circumstances in such a way that we can act as particles in the stream of personal consciousness.

This inwardly directed process of centration must, however, be accompanied by a piercing of the shell of our own ego, a process which may be described as de-centration (*décentration*). Like the cells of the human body, a well-developed sense of personal awareness and the entire personality can fulfil their function only through cohesion with others of their kind. Life presents itself to us as a plurality, and its value depends upon that realization. Only this can effect a propagation and diversification of personal awareness analogous to the law of increasing complexity which governs the evolution of all life.

Beyond this, there is a need for a link of a higher kind, for super-centration (*sur-centration*), which implies contact with a higher order whose existence is either to be surmised or comprehended by faith. Men have, after all, an innate urge to combine in larger societies and organizations, and our own age is particularly well-provided with evidence of a universal human process whereby man's unique nervous system is beginning to foster a cosmopolitan evolution—one which aspires to greater unity under the combined pressures of population growth and an increasing need for economic exchanges. While new nations are still coming into being, old groups are being transformed into new and the idea of supra-national units is in the ascendant. It is obvious that the progressive section of modern humanity is more eager than ever to belong to a larger order.[2]

The course of this evolution ought to place the individual under an obligation to devote himself to it, in what capacity soever, in order to further its development. By

[2] '*Un centre d'ordre supérieur nous attend,—déjà il apparaît—non plus seulement à côté, mais* au-delà *et* au-dessus *de nous mêmes.*' (*Cahiers* II, p. 63.)

so doing, he is only giving back what he has received as a sharer in progressive life-force.

In this sense, we are required to stake our lives, to risk life in order to gain it. So it was with all the great pioneers who were motivated by a fervent quest for knowledge: with the two Curies, who sacrificed their lives to the discovery of radium, with the many people who have forfeited their lives in medical or biological research, with the explorers Nansen and Scott, with the first cosmonauts, and with the countless others who have tried to win men for a cause. What, asked Teilhard, can we perceive in such dedication? Happiness of the most sublime kind, a profound joy in living, a fierce outpouring of life-force which can at last find an infinite field for expansion. 'Whoever has discovered, whether in an ideal or in some special task, the secret of serving the evolving Universe and identifying himself with it, for him the shadows (of doubt and fear) will disappear.'

Thoughts like these were not elaborated in Teilhard's study but distilled from the experience gained in a lifetime of exacting work. He acquired his scientific knowledge by exertion and by the conquest of doubt. Behind his unflagging spirit of inquiry one could sense the strength of his cosmic approach to life, the mental élan so characteristic of him. There is an element of tragedy in the fact that this strength exercised an effect on such a relatively small circle and could not be disseminated on a world-wide scale during his lifetime. It was left to posthumous publications to extend his sphere of influence.

Because Teilhard regarded a cosmic approach to life as the supreme form of happiness, he felt prompted to put forward certain precepts for living. Their ethical significance is such that they cannot be omitted from the present work, but they also reveal Teilhard the scientist in a highly characteristic light. While he undoubtedly meant his practical guidance to help others to become aware of this form of happiness and achieve it in their daily lives, he himself admitted that it could only take the form of general directives. Being subject to traits of character and individual circumstances of his own, the individual has ultimately to find his own way of establishing contact with the evolution of the Universe.

In the first place, Teilhard believed, we must not look for any extraneous reinvigoration, although psychical strength does accrue to us from material resources. Endeavours of the intellectual, artistic and moral sort are more important because we can expect them to contribute to the achievement of lasting happiness. 'We ought,' as the explorer Nansen once said, 'to regard our most important task in life as the discovery of our ego.'

Further, we should neither cut ourselves off from others, nor try to dominate them, nor be selfish in our love. The love that brings true happiness consists in common spiritual progress.

Finally, we must find some means (by dedicating ourselves to a task, idea, inquiry or undertaking) of devoting our lives to the progress of the world around us. This need not involve us in great voyages of exploration or feats of scientific research. It is enough if we pledge ourselves to a higher order, each according to his talent and ability. In this way, too, we learn to distinguish the important things from the less important and so contribute, even as minute particles, to the immense process of life.

Such ingredients of happiness may seem self-evident, but are we alert to them in our daily life? Certainly, Teilhard had good reason to pursue the problem of happiness as zealously as he pursued his research into the meaning of life. He found it indispensable to the continued development of personal consciousness that we should devote ourselves to it with profound joy.

'A passionate love of growth, of being, that is what we need.' Men are striving for a unity to which they themselves hold the key. Joint collaboration between science and technology has already outlined the way in which mankind is being subordinated to a higher process, and thereby more firmly united.

I believe that the potentialities for happiness which emerge from Teilhard's world of ideas have a most important bearing on the present situation. I am thinking in particular of the use of atomic weapons, which many see as a grave threat to the future of mankind. What can we do to obviate such a catastrophe? Few of us are in a position to influence events favourably by personal intervention, but does this mean we can do nothing at all? The answer to that is as follows:

In the first place, we can refrain from allowing technology, which is moving in the direction of world-wide union, to develop in a spiritual vacuum, that is to say, without spiritual fuel, without proper values and without reference to our knowledge of man. The developments of the past few decades have shown us that it would be irresponsible to leave the choice between existence and non-existence to a handful of experts. Never has man's destiny seemed more fragile than it does today, but never has it been more dependent on a belief in man.

In this highly precarious situation, we must bear in mind the reserves of humanism which have grown up where awareness of the danger is most highly developed, i.e. among some of the leading scientists of our day. Teilhard may seem unique in his faith, but he is no isolated case. Do not Einstein, Heisenberg, Bertrand Russell and Julian Huxley belong in his company, and has not Huxley recognized biology as a 'religion without revelation'?[3] Apart from these, scores of others are indulging in creative activity, inspired by faith of some kind. We ought not to underestimate the potential of this reserve of humanism, which can help us to overcome our indifference to world events. This much is certain: the future of mankind is utterly inconceivable without the development and mobilization of our moral and intellectual reserves. The history of the past few centuries —Reformation and Enlightenment—proves how greatly the fate of nations is governed by human ideals, and even, in the case of someone like Mahatma Gandhi, constructively influenced by individual men of faith. How much more could our existing knowledge of man's origins and capabilities help to replace the negative symptoms of our attitude toward the present crisis by more positive ones.

Vegetable physiology recognizes the law of heliotropy, whereby certain plants turn to face a source of light. We, too, can turn toward the light of spiritual energy by resolving to mobilize our reserves of humanism.

[3] Julian Huxley: *Religion without Revelation*, Max Parrish, London 1957.

In so far as this applies to scientists, I am aware that Teilhard's visionary and religious strength puts him in a special position. That is to say, the humanism engendered by science need not necessarily derive from the specific blend of religious and scientific experience which was characteristic of Teilhard. Even though he considered this desirable, his works do not convey a note of flat insistence. The very fact that he looked upon the science of man as a prime means of understanding evolution indicates that he aimed at a *universal* acceptance of his ideas. He was thinking of a 'human front', a mobilization of individually-based knowledge of the origin and destiny of man. His theories were meant to be accessible not only to the members of his own or other denominations, but to all. That is why I cannot concur with those who see him solely as an original reformer of the Catholic faith, nor recognize as constructive those of his critics who confine themselves to stressing his mixture of rational and visionary traits.

Teilhard was what so many of us will not and cannot be: a scientist who loved mankind and took a deliberate interest in its evolution. His contemporary importance derives not least from the fact that he kept his fingers on the pulse of our time and discovered new ways of accelerating it. In this respect, even his critics can go along with him. It is more than ever necessary to meet the momentous questions of our age constructively, thus ensuring that man's spiritual metabolism absorbs the nutritive material without which the future becomes inconceivable.

I can still picture Teilhard vividly, his finely chiselled features wearing an air of transparency, his whole figure seeming to radiate concentrated spirituality. When I saw him for the last time in the street in January 1955, just before I left for Spain, he was striding through the snow in his dark overcoat like a man hurrying to reach home. In April of the same year, the sad news reached me in Madrid that he had died on Easter Sunday.

THE END